COLLOTYPE
IN A
COTSWOLD TOWN

COLLOTYPE
IN A
COTSWOLD TOWN

An account of the
Cotswold Collotype Co. Ltd.
Specialist Printers
Wotton-under-Edge
Gloucestershire

by
Donald Emes

First published in the United Kingdom 1995
by Donald Emes.

© Copyright Donald Emes 1995

ISBN 0 9526345 0 3

Cover illustration: Frank Russell working on a collotype glass plate –
March 1957.

Produced by Alan Sutton Publishing Ltd, Stroud, Glos.
Printed in Great Britain
by WBC Ltd, Bridgend.

Contents

Appendices

List of Illustrations

Acknowledgements

Many local people were employed at Cotswold Collotype over the years, and very fine quality printing was produced. The mill has now been demolished, so I hope this book will serve as a reminder of the past happy years.

My thanks are due to Mr Philip Brooke (Brooke Bond involvement of the company and rotary collotype), Mr V. Jellings (drawings and records), Mr R. Alway (early family connections with Friths), Mrs Phoebe Johannessen, née Frith (her father's correspondence), and also to numerous other past employees who have helped in any way.

Finally, I wish to acknowledge the help given by my wife, Betty, whose suggestions and corrections have been very helpful throughout the preparation of this book.

The photographs are almost entirely from my own large collection taken while working for the company.

Donald Emes
June 1995

Introduction:

How the Collotype Process Worked

The process, designed in the 19th century, involves pouring light sensitive gelatin on to a plate glass base, although aluminium can now be used.

After drying, the base is mounted with negatives of the illustrations required and exposed to light.

The gelatin contracts, retaining a perfect reproduction of the negative; the light sensitive substances are washed out and the plate is dried and prepared for inking.

Then the gelatin is treated with a mixture of glycerin and water which swells it in inverse proportion to its light-hardness, bringing it to a state in which ink will be retained by it and can be transferred to paper.

The treatment is repeated until the exact tonal qualities of the original are matched.

The glycerin-soaking time must vary according to temperature, the age of the plate, the type of paper and ink, while at every stage the craftsman's skill is vital.

The first impression must be dull. To balance it, the plate is moistened with ammonia solution to open the grain to more ink, or with formaldehyde or alum solution to harden the surface and produce highlights.

A constant room temperature of 70°F must be maintained and an exact relative humidity level of 65%. The presses are hand inked and hand fed at about 250 sheets an hour.

The process takes time, and is best suited to short runs of a very high quality. It has to be, when a 10–12 colour process is not unusual and can be handled only at the rate of a colour a day.

How The Cotswold Publishing Company Started

The story of the Cotswold Publishing Company (CPC) which began about 1895 is closely linked with Friths of Reigate who were early publishers of picture postcards.

Their business stemmed from the introduction of photography, of which Frith was one of the pioneers, in addition to bringing great artistic merit to the process.

Until about the 1880s, picture postcards were printed on the continent by a process invented by the Frenchman Poitevan and known as collotype, a process incidentally very similar to photography.

As the Friths business grew, it is not surprising to learn that one of the brothers was sent to Europe to discover how the process worked.

In 1895 a mill was rented called Bristol Mill, Charfield to start collotype printing. The mill chosen was the largest of three built in 1812.

Water power was obtained by the same stream that operated Abbey, Langford and New Mills. The building was roofed with slate, in which dormer windows were incorporated, being four storeys high, and is still in good condition today.

On the ground floor at the present time some engineering work is in progress. The rest of the mill is used for storage.

It is not known exactly how the Reigate firm came to have an interest in a mill at Charfield, Gloucestershire.

What is certain, however, is that Frith and his photographers covered the length and breadth of the country with their cameras taking pictures for publication. Quite recently I was given a photograph measuring 18″ x 11″ taken in about 1880 of Abbey Mill! It is an albumen photograph in excellent condition today and would almost certainly have been taken by Friths. Few photographers would have used a camera taking a plate of that size.

Abbey Mill is only two miles from Charfield.

Original Management and Operatives

Mr Cyril Frith was installed as managing director and Mr F. Jeater and Mr C. R. Bagwell were transferred from Frith and Co. Ltd. at Reigate. As the printing presses had to be imported from France, a French printer was also brought in.

While working at the CPC, Mr H. J. Russell recalled to me a rather eccentric printer working at Charfield Mill from that country. A photograph of the staff was taken probably in 1907. The names of some are known, such as Mr C. Frith (managing director), Mr H. J. Russell, Mr C. Russell, Mr Bagwell and a member of the Harding family who lived at Charfield. I have a copy of this photograph, which was probably taken by either Mr Jeater or Mr S. Benson, both of whom worked at Charfield Mill.

The work undertaken was postcards, view books and probably some gold blocking. The last process was needed for printing the covers for the view books. Letterpress work was also undertaken.

Friths obtained some of their printers from London, where collotype printing was in progress for several years.

Mr Harry J. Russell was the first to join, in 1897. After a while he invited one of his younger brothers, Charles, to come for a holiday with a view to joining the company.

Evidently Charles was impressed and started at Charfield, leaving the London printers of Eyre & Spottiswoode where the two brothers had been employed.

In 1980 I met Mr S. Benson (son of F. J. Benson) who was a friend of Mr H. J. Russell, both living at Sunnyside, Charfield and closely involved with Charfield Congregational Chapel.

Mr Benson told me that his father, Francis Joseph, was a photographer of some standing and a colleague of the famous early photographer Francis Frith who died, aged 76, in Cannes and was buried in a Protestant cemetery there – he was the grandfather of Mr F. E. Frith who later became managing director of the CPC.

Mr Benson, who was living at Brockley, was invited to go to Charfield to help print postcards. Previously they were printed on the continent, probably in Saxony.

He agreed and the Charfield Mill was rented from Mr Stanley Tubbs (later Sir Stanley) and the business was started with Mr Jeater and Mr Bagwell coming from the Reigate works of F. Frith & Co.

Apart from printers, there would have had to be a platemaker, photographer, guillotine operator and other workers.

Mr Bagwell is known to have been a platemaker later at Britannia Mill, Wotton. He probably did the same job at Charfield. Mr Benson, being a photographer, carried on with the photographic and processing work needed. Mr H. J. Russell and his brother Charles were printers.

Mr Jeater most likely did the administrative work, packing and guillotining. Frank, the younger brother of the Russell family, quite possibly spent some time as a printer at Charfield.

After a while, Mr Benson left to start a business in portrait photography, first at Stroud then Bristol.

Mr Jeater most probably took on the photographic work of making the negatives for the collotype plates for printing postcards.

Unfortunately, the collotype business did not prosper under the leadership of Mr C. Frith and in 1907 Friths postcard work was returned to the continent and the business prepared to close down.

However, the courage and determination of three employees, Bagwell, Jeater and Russell, gave a stay of execution. They bought the business for next to nothing and carried on. Having lost Friths postcards, the local business was intensified and the outside photographic work was probably undertaken by Mr Jeater.

Mr Russell would have continued as a printer, Mr Bagwell as platemaker. A small number of local men and women employees were retained.

A Change of Name and Expansion of Business

After some progress the name of the business was changed in 1909 from F. Frith & Co. to The Cotswold Publishing Company.

Besides postcard work, prospectuses for schools were printed. These usually took the form of a sepia blank page booklet. The pages being either tied in with cord or stitched and with a decorated gold blocked cover. The titled collotype prints were stuck centrally on each page.

Although few of these examples remain, I have one for a school prospectus for Katharine Lady Berkeley's Grammar School, Wotton-under-Edge, and there is another copy in the Wotton Museum.

The headmaster used some of these as an advertisement when, at that time, boarders were taken at the headmaster's house.

The Company Moves to Wotton-Under-Edge

In 1912 the company met another setback. The landlord, Tubbs Lewis, announced that they needed the premises for their own use and gave notice to quit.

A search began for a suitable building. One was found just off the Coombe road at Wotton-under-Edge, called Britannia Mill. It was a four-storey building. The sky was visible right from the ground floor when all the trap doors in the floors were open. The date 1693 was carved on a beam on the second floor.

It had been a fulling mill in the heyday of wool on the Cotswold hills. The Salvation Army used it for their meetings.

For a time engineering work was carried on there and finally it was a sauce factory making 'Cotswold Sauce'.

The infestation of flies was a lasting reminder of those 'saucy' days!

Adapting the Premises

Before any printing could start, the mill had to be thoroughly cleaned. Although mains water was available, mains drainage was not. Lavatories were provided – these were of a wooden construction with galvanised roofing. The buckets were limed and were emptied weekly. One of the young printers did this job and received 2/6 (12½p) extra in his wages for his trouble. Later, when mains drainage was installed, these lavatories were converted into a cycle shed.

The printing presses could, of course, be dismantled but even so the cast-iron side frames and rollers required several men to lift them. Everything was loaded on to farm wagons, transported the 2½ miles to Wotton, off-loaded and manhandled through the double doors. Before re-assembly the earth floor had to be overlaid with tarmac to bed down the machines – a solution by no means satisfactory, but cheap. At the end of a very long day the three directors and others walked the 2½ miles back to Charfield. It was the middle of the winter.

It is hard to imagine what had to be installed in order to provide a self-contained printing company, such as a camera room and darkroom with running water. (Drainage was into the brook which ran by the side of the mill.)

A platemaking department was needed in which heated boxes had to be installed for the 'cooking' of the plates and some lighting. Gas jets were also a necessity to keep the press beds warm. Running water had to be extended to several parts of the mill and a boiler house had to be built. The boiler may have been in use at the Charfield Mill as one would have been required there. This was necessary for the heating of the mill and was situated on the right-hand side facing the mill. Stone steps beside the boiler house led to the main entrance and first floor. Eventually steam heating pipes were installed by Terretts of Kingswood.

The platemaking room had a plaster ceiling in order to prevent dust settling on collotype plates in the making. Large frames containing the sensitized plate and negatives were lowered by a hoist and taken outside to a glasshouse for exposing. Most of the remaining ceilings were simply canvas nailed to the rafters and with sheets of white paper pasted on. It was surprising how many years this arrangement lasted.

The water wheel had long since disappeared so power came from a gas engine driving a flat leather belt to overhead shafting through the press room. Gas was supplied by using anthracite and the system worked very well.

At Charfield a water wheel supplied the power. This type of engine deserves a much more detailed description. Suffice it to say that a printer started at 7.30am to get the gas-making plant operating. When the rest of the printers arrived at 8am they pulled on the leather belt and started the engine. The engine room was located on the ground floor in an extension to the main building. Above this, on the first floor, were the offices. The camera room was on the second floor.

The Work of the New Premises

Hours worked were from 8 a.m. to 6 p.m. Monday to Friday, and 8 a.m. to 1 p.m. on Saturdays. Work undertaken was largely postcards, booklets, gold blocking and sometimes large pictures for framing. I have seen one of Berkeley Castle in this locality. Soon after the move to Wotton, bromide postcards were also printed. This work was carried out on the second floor of an annexe which appears to have been added at a later date. A large lead-lined wooden sink was made to hold the various dishes used for the bromide printing. Some cards were black and white, others were sepia toned.

The cards were printed in strips of six and usually in runs of 144 cards of each subject. Collotype cards retailed at one penny each, bromide cards sold for two pence. Two finishes were available – semi-matt and glossy. The latter surface was glazed on ¼″ plate glass after the surface had been swabbed with a glazing solution called 'BANGO', made by the Vanguard Manufacturing Company. These, we can refer to them as glasses, were placed around the room, propped against the wall and stairway rail to the second floor. Here the prints gradually dried and detached themselves from the glasses.

When drying, the strips made a cracking sound as the highly polished surface left the glass, hence the name 'BANGO' given to the glazing solution. The prints sometimes dried too quickly and the glaze was rather spoilt by part of the bromides drying irregularly and causing semi-circular cracks in the surface.

The semi-matts were an easier proposition; they were laid on frames of butter muslin and allowed to dry naturally.

On joining the company I was intrigued by bags containing cotton wool tied over the outlet of the taps used for bromide printing. Their purpose was to collect any particles of rust in the water supply which could cause unsightly blue spots on the surface of the sepia bromide cards.

Local views were printed (as also in due course – see later the Frith series) and the bromide cards had the conventional postcard backing on them supplied by the photographic paper manufacturers. I have a photographic print of Tetbury printed on paper with the Friths style of postcard backing.

Printing of the cards was carried out by two people, one of whom did the exposing on a gaslight printer, this being the only form of lighting available. The second person did the developing, fixing and washing. When the prints were dry they were cut into single cards which promptly allowed them to curl the view side.

In order to flatten them, a girl using a shaped piece of wood about 6″ x 3″ x ½″ with one long edge tapered drew the cards singly face down under the prepared edge. This imparted a reverse curl. These operations were necessary to produce the cards lying flat which then only took a short time to band.

The floors of the darkroom and offices were treated with a bituminous compound laid by Italian POWs in the district after the First World War. This prevented the seepage of water from the darkroom above and fumes from rising from the gas engine below.

There were seven collotype presses, one of which was converted to letterpress and used for printing the standard size backing on the postcard sheets, which consisted of 36 cards of 5½" x 3½".

The Wotton-Under-Edge Production Staff

Mr Bagwell was the platemaker and he set up the negatives into sheets ready to expose on to the collotype plate.

Mr Jeater was in charge of the office and made out the postcard orders. These were written in beautiful handwriting. He also cut up the postcard sheets into single cards. The wages were also made up by him but someone else handed them to the staff.

Mr H. J. Russell (Snr.), originally a printer, managed the company and worked in the negative retouching department. Charles and Frank Russell and Charles Beale were collotype printers. Jack Goscombe and Harry Russell Jnr. were being taught the printing methods.

William White ran the letterpress while Edith Hollister, Phyllis Wyatt and other girls laid the paper on the printing presses for printing. They also did various finishing jobs such as spotting, tissuing postcards and packing.

A few personal notes about some of the people employed at this time might be interesting.

Charles Russell stayed with the company past retiring age. He was a printer but could turn his hand to many jobs about the factory. When the boiler needed descaling, prior to the factory inspector's visit, he came in on a Bank holiday to do this work himself.

His brother Frank went to the U.S.A. after the 1914–18 war but was invited to return. This he did in the early 1930s and remained with the company until his retirement in 1957.

Jack Goscombe, after leaving the Grammar School, started his collotype training in 1915. He became works manager and later works director after Mr H. Russell Jnr. retired in 1963.

Charles Beale came to this district from Derby to work on the railway, but after a short time he came to work for Friths at the

Charfield mill where be became a collotype printer. After a while he decided to take an insurance job, probably at the time when Friths sold the business. Later he returned to printing and went to London, soon after that firm closed following a disastrous fire, and he returned to Bemrose at Derby.

In 1915 he was invited to join the CPC and accepted. Later he joined the forces but returned after the war ended in 1918. He was due for retirement at the outbreak of the Second World War but was asked to continue with the company, finally retiring in the late 1940s at the age of 72.

The Great War

The 1914–18 war came at an unfortunate time for the company because it had only settled in Wotton a few years earlier. Materials were severely restricted and some employees were called up or volunteered. William White was one. While in France he met Harry Russell Jnr. who had left the Grammar School and by putting a year or two on his age had joined the Gloucester Regiment.

Property Extensions and Acquisitions

A wise move by the directors was to buy up cheaply a number of cottages around the mill. This proved very useful when space to build an annexe was required in the early 1930s. There was also quite a useful piece of land in front of the mill, most of which was used as allotments. Several sheds and the glasshouse – used to expose the collotype plates to daylight – were erected here in due course.

There were trapdoors between the floors of the main building which could be opened to allow the plates to be lowered by means of the hoist. Goods from the guillotine and packing departments on the first floor were also moved in this way. The LMS goods vehicle was too wide to gain access, so the driver would reverse until just one corner came through the open double doors of the ground floor. This just allowed the goods to be loaded direct. The hoist gear was on the top floor and was also used to bring goods up to the various departments. After the 1914–18 war, when the few servicemen returned, more work was required.

The Frith Connection Restored

About 1920 an agreement was reached with F. Frith & Co. of Reigate to restart printing their postcards. Since the selling of the Charfield business in 1907, their postcards had been printed on the continent. Also at this time Mr F. E. Frith, who had served in the 1914–18 war, returned and later became a director of the Cotswold Publishing Co. He then became the youngest of four company directors. His career in the army was quite distinguished as the following citation shows:-

> MILITARY CROSS FOR 2ND LIEUT. F. E. FRITH
> 2nd Lieut. F. Frith R.F.A., eldest son of Mr & Mrs. Eustace Frith, has been awarded the Military Cross.
>
> The official announcement states that the distinction was confirmed for conspicuous gallantry during operations near Ypres. He was with his battery during severe shelling on July 16th & 18th, when many casualties occurred. His coolness and disregard of danger were most marked and set a fine example in the ranks.
>
> He also assisted in saving ammunition from a 'dump' which had just received a direct hit and where fire had started.

The work done by Mr Frith at the CPC was organising the printing of furniture catalogues which had just started as a new venture. After training on the continent, he worked in the negative retouching department. He also had his own office on the first floor. The business started to build up again and the company was making progress and employing more people.

Good Management, Good Work Force, Growing Business

Mr Frith and Mr H. J. Russell were able to pass on their skills of negative retouching to the girls employed in this department. Both Mr Russell's daughter and Frank Wathen's sister were employed here.

Perhaps at this stage some information concerning the three original directors would be interesting.

Mr Jeater, the oldest of the three directors, came from Reigate where he worked for Frith & Co. He probably did some

Frith & Co., Charfield – *c.* 1907. Back row, left to right: Mr H.J. Russell, next three unknown, Mr C.R. Bagwell, Mr C. Frith, others unknown

The four original directors

Mr C.R. Bagwell

Mr F. Jeater

Mr H.J. Russell

Mr F.E. Frith

Charfield Mill

The Cotswold Publishing Company – 1912

Wotton-Under-Edge – *c.* 1900. Centre building bought by the company in 1912. Stream ran in front of the willows.

Late 1920s. Left to right: Elsie Cornock, Doris Russell, Emily Sharp, Charles Russell, Charles Beale, Harry Russell Jnr.

Taken mid-1920s before the annexe was built. Note steps to main entrance at side of boiler house. The glasshouse (foreground) was originally used to expose collotype plates. Course of stream followed stone wall. Measurements of building: front width – 44 ft; offices and darkroom – 20 ft, tapering to 10 ft at rear; height (excluding roof) – 44 ft; boiler house – 14 ft; glasshouse over darkroom and office block – 22 ft x 10 ft.

Edith Smith and Alec Lusty preparing strips of bromide cards for drying – 1920s.

Some employees – 23 April 1929. Back row, left to right: William White, Miss Malone, Edith Dolman, Hilda Gibbard, unknown, Edith Smith. Front row: Bert Tilley, May Carter, Blanche Wyatt.

c. 1933. Left to right: R. Woodward, H. Cooper, L. Newman, M. Chappell, J. Allen, J. Goscombe, L. Smith, G. Thurkettle, F. Wathen, E. Carter, C. Arthurs, H. Jones.

Late 1930s. Left to right: D. Emes (author), E. Hurlock, W. White, J. Goscombe, G. Underhill, R. Woodward, D. Spill, L. Cullimore.

photographic work besides other duties. As he dealt with guillotining, setting out the orders and the running of the office at the CPC he almost certainly did this work with Friths at Reigate. He also titled all the postcard negatives. This he did in the main office. The negatives were brought down to him from the retouching department.

He travelled to work with Mr Russell, firstly by motorcycle and side-car, later by car. As a keen organist he played the organ in Charfield Church.

William White considered him to be a very efficient man. He used to cut up sheets of postcards and write out the despatch labels, then he would place the orders with the postcards and labels, memorizing the number of cards for each customer.

There was no telephone whilst he was a director and all urgent messages were sent out by telegram from Wotton Post Office. These were taken by any young member of the staff available (sometimes me!).

His wife died in 1913 and was buried in Charfield old churchyard. In the late 1920s he remarried a member of staff, Miss Lillian Kent, and she ran the letterpress printing for the backing of postcards. In those days the sheets of postcards had to be taken to the office for the imprints to be checked against the orders.

While writing this book I was able to contact this lady who gave me a lot of useful information dealing with the time when she worked for the company. After Mr Jeater's death she remarried and lived at Weston-super-Mare. He died in 1931 at the age of 71.

Mr Bagwell, who was probably the platemaker both at Charfield and Wotton, was a bachelor and always wore a winged collar. He also came from Reigate and his home was thought to have been at Beer in Devon. In his early days he lived with Mr and Mrs. Morton in Long Street, Wotton. (These premises, at the time of writing, are a hairdressing salon called Scissor Scene.) He had a brother and sister, also nephews and nieces.

A story is told how one day a representative for a paper company called at the CPC. It so happened that Mr Bagwell met him and after conversation he discovered it was his nephew who, at that time, was living at Bourne End.

Sport and music were Mr Bagwell's pastimes and he opened his home to youths who were also interested.

For a time he lived at the top of the CPC drive in a house called 'Rosemary'. On Saturday nights he held musical evenings and was interested in, and followed, the local football teams. I have several photos of him with teams of which he was president.

Sometimes Mr Bagwell invited Jack Goscombe to spend the weekend with him at 'Rosemary'.

As he grew older he left this house and moved to a property very near the Earl Grey Inn, Wortley Road named 'The Hollies' after a holly tree planted in the front garden. The house then had a small orchard at the rear.

By coincidence, a lady called Miss Malone, who worked at the CPC, had lived in the house previously until her mother died. It was she who had planted the holly tree.

Another duty Mr Bagwell performed was taking the wages to the staff. The money was put into stiff red envelopes about postcard size. After the employee had checked the contents he collected the envelope for re-use (economy!).

He was a very early riser and started work long before anyone else, but would leave about mid-afternoon.

A year or two later, after Mr Jeater's death, he retired, living for a number of years at, but never moving from, 'The Hollies'.

As time went on, his health deteriorated and the running of the house and garden was too much for him. Mr Bert Watts undertook this job working full-time, and his wife also helped.

The Watts family lived very close, almost opposite Mr Bagwell's house, but eventually they moved in with their son Jim, thus saving a lot of running to and fro. Finally Mr Bagwell died in the early 1940s leaving the house to Mr and Mrs Watts.

Mr H. J. Russell Snr. was the youngest of the three original directors. He was a Londoner and came to Charfield as a collotype printer from Eyre & Spottiswoode, London, and lived at 'Sunnyside', New Street, Charfield.

He started to attend Charfield Congregational Chapel where it is said he found a firm basis for his faith and from then onwards he worked untiringly for the Christian faith. His wife also worked with him in the Sunday School, together with their son and two daughters. They sang in the choir and his daughter-in-law was the organist.

As soon as possible, when finances allowed, he bought a

motorcycle combination. This he kept at Mr F. G. Benson's, who lived near Mr Russell, at the other end of the terraced houses and had room to garage it.

Mr H. J. Russell was general manager and besides working as a negative retoucher he undertook the very responsible task of 'passing' the first good collotype sheet against the originals.

He took a keen interest in football and played when possible.

He brought into the company young men he thought suitable. Many remained until retirement at 65 years of age.

He was always willing to experiment with new ideas. He foresaw the advantages of rotary collotype and if the finances had allowed he would have been trying this method of printing many years before it was introduced in the company. The advantages were the speed of producing the plate, together with its mobility, as against the heavy glass plate; also the ease of exposing to artificial light and the absolute accuracy of the gelatin coating.

The number of runs off the press per day was a tremendous increase, being in the region of 5,000 as against 750 originally. This was essential in the production of sale catalogues.

The 1939–45 war depleted the staff, some joining the Forces and others leaving for essential war work. The practical knowledge of the process Mr H. J. Russell had gained over the years proved very useful and helped in holding the business together. He stayed with the company until the younger members returned from the Forces and older ones were released from war work.

After a very short retirement, Mr H. J. Russell Snr. died in 1948.

Company Progress From 1920

By 1920 the plates were no longer taken outside for exposure. A wooden structure was built over the darkroom and offices, that is, at the end of the mill nearest the stream. This part of the factory was probably a later addition to the mill.

It was about 2½–3ft lower on all floors and one floor less in height. This meant the exposing room was built into the roof of the darkroom.

Entrance was made through the wall of the platemaking department of the far end wall nearest the brook. This saved an awful lot of work lowering the plates on the hoist for exposing in the outside glasshouses.

The company was gradually recovering from the War and with the postcard work from Friths it was slowly expanding. Whenever possible any suitable collotype press that was for sale cheaply was bought and stored.

Some Site Development

Fortunately, accommodation was not a great problem. When the company had moved to Wotton there were a number of pigsties on the right-hand side just past the entrance gates leading to the mill. These were removed and a large garage built allowing several spare collotype machines to be stored. This also left enough room for Mr Russell to garage his car.

The whitewash marks on the boundary wall can still be faintly seen where the sties were built.

A little further down still on the right-hand side was a two-storey building which also contained some machinery. Flammable liquids were stored here at a short distance from the main building in case of fire.

An entrance through the boundary wall led to a pathway from the town to Synwell.

Just above the drive entrance on the left were a number of cottages. A row backed on to Valley Road and another row abutted these at right angles. These two rows made two sides of a square with their gardens in the middle. These properties were aptly called 'The Square'. The houses were brick built and not in very good condition; they were demolished in 1960.

Adjoining these properties and Valley Road were two stone-built semi-detached cottages facing the north-west end of the mill. In one of these lived the Kent family – brothers Charlie and Bill. Their sister, Lilian, also lived there in the 1920s. She worked for the company running the letterpress and married Mr Jeater, one of the original directors.

A few paces further down Valley Road was another pair of semi-detached houses of the same size and style. They were end on to the mill and stood back a little away from and having their entrances on to Valley Road. Their gardens ran right down to the end of the mill.

Buying these properties proved very useful, as the annexe to the mill could then be built on the bottom part of these gardens.

All the cottages and gardens just mentioned were owned only by the original three directors. Eventually two directors, Mr Bagwell and Mr Jeater, sold their share to Mr H. J. Russell Snr.

The Friths in Wotton-Under-Edge

Mr and Mrs Frith lived in a house facing the mill when they first came to Wotton and their two children, John and Phoebe, were born there. The house is still standing, at the time of writing, but it is unoccupied. It was bought by the company in the late 1950s together with a large orchard. On this land the Brookeside Gravure Factory was built in 1960. Whether the orchard belonged to the house originally I cannot say.

Mr Frith then changed houses with Mr Isaac, moving to the bottom of Long Street (it is currently a cycle shop). A little later Mr Frith took tenancy of 'Hindleppe', Haw Street, owned by the Foundation Governors of the Grammar School. Here he lived until his retirement in 1959, when he moved to a bungalow at Coombe Valley Lakes. This had a large garden and was in a very quiet area, about a mile out of the town.

1926 General Strike: Tough Conditions – Then Recovery

The general strike of 1926 was another upset for the company and meant further economies. For several years Mr Frith had run a car but he sold it at this time and never took up driving again.

However, by the end of that decade the company again made progress. More postcard work was coming in from J.V. Valentines, Harvey Bartons, Raphael Tuck & Son, and several others.

'Fire!'

On Saturday, 21 September 1929 a small fire started in the engine room. It was first discovered at about 7.30 a.m. The fire engine was called and after a while the fire was put out and production was continued. A social event was going to be held in the afternoon for the newly acquired fire engine to be named. As can well be imagined the firemen had cleaned the engine beautifully in preparation for the show. Having to attend the fire meant all their work had to be done again.

As the engine had to 'fly' to that fire on the day it was appropriately named 'Firefly'. Inadvertently our company was responsible for the name.

In later years the engine was sold and another took its place. Fortunately for Wotton the engine, having been bought by an enthusiast, came on the market again. The Shellard family who are interested in old vehicles attended the sale, bought it and so it returned to its original home.

Two of the Shellard girls worked for the company, Janice and Ann, so we had another link with the fire engine.

Cameo Cards

A popular item produced at this time were Cameo Cards. These were a dozen or more half postcard size prints put in a small packet bearing the place name and titles of the enclosed cards. To give added strength to the packet, they were machine stitched each side. This work was carried out by one of the girls using a 'Singer' treadle sewing machine. Lengths of these packets were stitched up both sides then cut into singles ready for the cards to be inserted.

Cleanliness is Next to Godliness

The collotype presses had to be washed thoroughly each night to prevent the ink drying on the rollers, etc. The girl who laid the sheets of paper on the presses carried out this work. It meant washing the rollers and ink slabs with paraffin. Clean rag was used for this purpose and was kept in a large locker under the stairs leading to the top floor. Mr R. Morley from Potters Pond supplied the rags, carrying them to the mill in a huge sack.

Before the Days of Mobile Phones

Communication between floors was by the 'blower'. This method used metal piping connecting each floor and the office, terminating in a combined earpiece and a detachable whistle. A person wishing to make a call would take out the whistle and blow into the tube. This would sound on the floor selected. The whistle was then removed, the call answered and the whistle replaced. When calls were made to individuals there was a whistling code to ensure the correct person took the call – particularly useful when press girls were hanging paper in the drying racks on the second floor.

This method of communication may have been responsible for the phrase 'get on the blower' which later meant 'to use the telephone'.

Lighting

Gas lighting was originally used. However, the mill was later wired for electricity powered by a dynamo driven by the engine. The light bulbs were coloured blue and gave only a poor light, so some gas lighting was left. Mr Jeater and Mr Frith preferred it and the platemaker needed it when returning in the evening to remove plates from the washing out tank.

Office Modernisation

Mr Jeater died in 1931. Mr Frith then took over his duties and reorganised the office. A telephone was installed avoiding journeys to the post office and made for speedier communication between customers. A lady secretary was employed who typed the letters dictated by Mr Frith. The putting out of orders was also her responsibility.

Job Allocations

Mr Frith still worked in the retouching department when time permitted, as did Mr Russell. They advised the negative retouching girls (clouds on finished postcards were often artificially sprayed on the negative).

By this time the company was expanding, a greater variety of work was being undertaken and more staff were employed.

Mr Russell was increasingly tied to the printing side as he passed all the printers' first sheets with the originals. He also made all the negatives until in the early 1930s this became a full-time job.

Mr Frith proof-read all the letterpress work before printing.

When Mr Bagwell retired someone had to be employed and trained for the platemaking. Mr Russell helped out there for a while.

Mr Frank Russell, as previously stated, rejoined the company after a spell in America. He was a valuable trained collotype printer. At one time there were three Russells as collotype printers – Mr Frank Russell, his brother Charles, and Harry, who was the son of Mr H. J. Russell Snr., one of the original directors.

The Surroundings

The south side of the mill could be very pleasant in the summer-time. A stream ran by the side of the mill, branches of willows touched the water in places, and the occasional kingfisher could be seen.

In the summer holidays, children would dam the stream and make a shallow bathing pool.

Once a badly injured otter was caught, put out of its suffering and the skin cured and retained by a member of the staff. On the rare occasion, a few small trout escaped from Coombe lakes and passed into the mill stream. The field was quite steep and the grass had to be cut with a scythe and the hay turned by farm workers using wooden hand rakes.

Even foxes used to be seen crossing the field in broad daylight. Now it is covered with houses.

The Business Expands – Process Improvements

Owing to the rapid increase in business a lean-to building was erected on the north-west side of the mill. This building was about half the size of the printing room and contained three presses, two were collotype and one a converted collotype to take letterpress. A cropper (a small printing machine) and cases of type were also housed here. This pressroom took part of the gardens of the two stone-built cottages belonging to the original three directors.

The space left by the removal of the typesetting and letterpress department in the main press room was taken by another collotype press.

A staircase was made from the new annexe to the first floor but it was so steep as to be highly dangerous and its use was finally forbidden.

With the increased work, difficulties were experienced in exposing sufficient plates to daylight, especially during the winter months.

An additional source of artificial illuminant had to be considered. Finally, mercury vapour tubes were chosen. These could be placed near the collotype plates without overheating. This was considered a great step forward as, until this time, all plates had to be exposed to daylight. Sometimes in the winter months the plates had to be put out the second day.

Whenever possible, the plates were given a certain amount of exposure to daylight, as the printers preferred this light if possible.

About the same time, artificial light was installed in the camera room for making negatives from prints sent in by customers. This also proved a great success. In fact, with the workload increasing it would have been difficult to produce the greater number of negatives required.

A new venture taken by the company was the printing of illustrations for books. Mr J. Beck was the agent and the company took quite a lot of this type of work.

His son, Geoffrey Beck, also intended entering the business with his father and he spent a few weeks with our company. This gave him an insight into the process and the work most suitable for collotype. He stayed a few weeks and lived with Mr and Mrs Frith during this time. However, he did not join the business, but finally entered the Methodist Ministry. After the war he visited this part of the country preaching at a local church and we made contact again.

New Printing Ventures – The Field Enlarges

Perhaps at this point it would be interesting to recall the type of work being undertaken other than the run-of-the-mill postcards. These illustrations were often for well-known book publishers such as Faber & Faber, Macmillan, etc. The de-luxe edition of H. V. Morton's *In the Steps of the Master* was an interesting commitment and included a number of pictures of the Holy Land. We made the photographic prints from negatives supplied. This helped fire my long standing ambition to visit the Holy Land and a few years later this was fulfilled by a holiday in Israel.

Portraits by Sir William Rothenstein proved a difficult challenge to print. The originals were drawings with coloured chalks on a variety of papers, of different textures and colours. Very often to 'lift' the drawing of the subject from the background, when making the negative, accentuated the texture of the paper which created an unpleasant effect.

Sir William lived at Bisley and the last portrait to complete the job was of Edward, Prince of Wales. Mr Russell collected this drawing and I was fortunate to accompany him as it was in the quiet period.

Mr Russell, who had made negatives, was a great help to me, as I lacked experience of this kind of work. However, by using various filters and films, the desired negatives were produced.

A similar subject we reproduced was a portrait of HRH Prince Philip many years later.

One Hundred Years of English Women's Dress was quite a big job needing a lot of illustrations. Many were taken from large books and were quite old.

The company was asked to reproduce these illustrations again in the 1950s. This we did as most of the negatives were still in a very good condition.

A glasshouse used originally for plate exposure in front of the mill was converted into an exposing room. This helped a great deal as it gave more space to handle large awkward originals. The small copying room in general use was far too small for this kind of work.

Illustrations for a book called *The Duke of Portland* were also printed. If my memory is correct, this dealt with a large number of horse paintings.

The History of Chinese Art, *Eyeless in Gaza*, *The Duke of Windsor* de-luxe edition are others which come to mind.

The plate frames together with three plates, i.e. frame glass, negative glass and collotype plate, were carried out to the exposing room. Later, a trolley was made carrying two plate frames at a time. This speeded up the time of transfer and saved labour.

The plates had to be kept in close contact in order to produce a sharp image and this necessitated the plates being forced into contact by wedging them under bars in the frames.

A wooden mallet was used to drive the wedges under the bars to get sufficient contact. For a time, screw pressure was used but this proved unsatisfactory and plates were sometimes broken. When they did break, there was quite a crash.

Engine/Motor Care

After every fourteen days the engine had to be decarbonised. This was done during the lunch hour by one of the printers. Exhaust gases were expelled outside the building. The outlet was moved several times because the fumes entered the offices above.

This engine was used until the end of the 1939–45 war when the business was acquired by the Berkshire Printing Company, a subsidiary of Brooke Bond.

They introduced an electric motor to drive the shafting. A few years later each press had its own motor, allowing printers to run their presses at a speed to suit the type of work they were printing. Some plates required a longer period between impressions being taken to recoup moisture.

Dispatch

The printed orders were dispatched by railway and the LMS lorry called several times a week to transport the work to Charfield Station. Local work for Harvey Bartons of Bristol was taken in by Wyatt, Carriers of Wotton. They also took the guillotine knives to Kears to be sharpened.

Fun, Games and Tea

The boiler was fired by breeze (very small coke, mostly dust) which was transported on the company's handtruck by two juniors, from the gas works next door.

We had to pile the truck full to overflowing for the company, but if any was wasted on the return journey, the gas manager soon became cross. It was hard to be a winner on this job!

As there were a few young men staying for the lunch hour, we used to play football in the field by the side of the mill if the weather was suitable. This field was quite steep and had a stream running at the bottom – as one can guess, several boys ended up in it.

To get a football was a bit of a problem as money was short in those days. However, one was obtained by saving Oxo cube wrappers as a number of us had this drink at lunch times.

Alternatively, if the weather was bad, a tea chest would be turned upside down and used as a table. Card games such as rummy were usually played.

All through the life of the company an hour was allowed for lunch. Most of the staff lived in or near the town and could get home for meals but a few came from Charfield and Kingswood.

In the summer a bat would be made and again a tea chest used as wickets. This game was played in front of the mill; the 'wickets' were placed against the double doors outside the machine shop.

A gas ring was provided on the second floor, where the finishing of the work was done, so this was used at lunch time to boil water for our hot drinks.

For some years there was no gas ring in the office, so it was my duty to take a kettle of hot water to the office for Mr Frith's China tea. If the weather was fine, he would stand at the top of the stone steps, leading to the checking-in clock, drinking it. He also smoked a hand-rolled cigarette made with Wills' Gold Flake tobacco.

We were allowed a ten-minute break in the morning and five minutes in the afternoon.

Access and Transport

A job that often had to be done was repairing what was known as the drive. This was the road from the entrance gates to the mill. As the road had never been properly made up for years, potholes continually appeared, especially as it was on a slope.

The material used for the repair work was coke clinker from the boiler. This was well rolled in with a large stone roller.

The outside windows were also painted and the person painting them had a rope fastened around his body and secured through the open window from inside while he was on the ladder. These jobs were carried out by the young men of the company during slack periods.

As the firm possessed no vehicle in the 1930s, transportation to the town was carried out on one or other of the two trucks available, a sack or hand truck.

The latter needed two people to push and it was used for taking parcels of postcards to the post office. If I remember rightly, 1,000 cards cost one shilling and three pence postal rate, this made one parcel.

As I walked past the post office on my way home to Kingswood, I was sometimes asked to take postcard parcels for posting. These were quite heavy and I was allowed to leave five minutes earlier. It came as a great relief when I could afford a secondhand bicycle and give up this job. The parcels were roped together and slung over one shoulder. Two shoulders if I was unlucky!

Two incidents involving myself come to mind. Having delivered the parcels to the post office, the truck being empty, I decided to run back with it. On Thomas's corner a wheel came off and ran into the Falcon Inn. Fortunately for me no damage was done!

The second incident was connected with the sack truck. After taking parcels to the post office, I forgot the truck. Next morning a man who worked at the ironmongers, next to the post office, returned it. I wasn't allowed to forget this incident for some time!

Air Brushing

As more orders were received, it was found necessary to have additional airbrushes installed as they were used for negative and print retouching.

School brochures, which were often printed, needed photographs updated and figures had to be retouched for views needed for postcards.

Typical instructions from one customer, Mr Catling, were 'please add curtains and pull up the boy's socks' to be effected with the airbrush!

Second World War

1939 saw the threat and outbreak of war. Work became short and for a period the mill was put on three days a week.

When war was actually declared, raw materials were curtailed and later the staff had to be cut down.

Mr Frith's son, John, having just left college and soon to enter the Services, joined the company for a short while. His duties were in the offices helping his father. A few months later he joined the RAF and was selected for training as a fighter pilot on Spitfires.

Those of military age joined the Armed Forces. I joined the RAF in the photographic section. Other members of the company were transferred to work essential to the war effort.

Several went to Parnells at Yate, Tubbs Lewis and Brooke Bond tea packing at Watsome, Charfield. One man was William White who had served in the 1914–18 war and was our guillotine operator: he was sent to Charfield.

The factory had been a milk collecting depot of Cadbury's but had closed and the work taken to Frampton-on-Severn.

Seeds of the Brooke Bond Partnership

The Brooke Bond Tea Company brought some of their key staff from their London factory but also employed local people.

A van load of tea labels was sent to Charfield but when unloaded it was discovered that the sheets had not been cut up as separate labels ready for the packing machines. Berkshire Printing Co. Reading also had its problems and it was reported that someone there remarked, 'Oh, send the sheets down, Ronnie Cecil will get round it somehow.'

Mr Cecil's delight can be imagined when William White offered to do the job back at Britannia Mill.

Next morning a telephone call from Reading made light of the 'How did you get on with the labels?'

Beginnings of the Berkshire Connection

Mr Cecil described the business at Wotton as being one of the very few collotype printers which interested the directors of the Berkshire Printing Co. (BPC), all of whom were dedicated printers at heart.

A visit was arranged immediately, as a result of which the CPC was acquired by the BPC, firstly, to maintain collotype, the finest of all printing processes, and secondly to provide the basis for diversifying into Gravure in the West Country.

More War Time Changes – Our Workers Cope

At this time Phoebe Frith finished college and wanted a job until she was old enough to join the Forces, so she came to work at the CPC While with the company she helped in a variety of jobs.

She made negatives under Mr Russell's direction and also did some packing. When the need arose she fed the plain sheets into the press operated by George Thurkettle. He had joined the company some years earlier from Harvey Barton's of Bristol, as a collotype printer. Mr Frith found her a great help in setting up negatives for printing.

She eventually joined the WAAF and served in the Meteorological Section.

Staff working at the company at this time were Phyllis Wyatt, Edith Smith, Hilda Gibbart, George Thurkettle, Charles Russell and Charles Beale. Mr H. Russell Jnr. was transferred to the Berkshire Printing Co. Reading on essential war work.

E.S. & A. Robinson of Bristol approached the company regarding printing facsimile work. This could be undertaken as it was for the American market and brought dollars to this country. Jack Goscombe was released from Parnells to undertake the printing.

Some of the earliest pictures were reproductions of the paintings *Magnolias* by Evelyn Stewart and *Lady with the Harp* by Lawrence Campbell Taylor. *Pines on the Dunes* was also printed.

E.S. & A. Robinson supplied the glass negatives, which had already been used for earlier editions. The retouchers who came to make corrections to the negatives were Mr Norman Hardisty and Mr Eyles.

A little later on the BPC supplied a suitable camera from which colour negatives could be made – up to about 16" x 18".

The company was also printing a series of pictures for the Ministry of Information of 15" x 12" size. This series covered the Services – Army, Navy and Air Force – and also the various sports and leisure activities as well as many occupations.

As materials were made available the company struggled to do what work they could. By the end of the war, members of the staff were being released from essential war work and the Armed Forces

Retirement of Mr H. J. Russell

Mr H. J. Russell Snr. had reached retirement age, but he wanted to see all the staff who had served in the Forces and been directed to essential war work return before he left. His son, Harry (Junior), was made a director of the company on 8 May 1946 on the retirement of his father.

This ended a long working life in collotype for Mr H. J. Russell Snr., coming from Eyre & Spottiswoode in 1898 to work for Frith & Co. at Charfield as a printer.

He put in much hard work when Friths sold the business to Mr Bagwell, Mr Jeater and himself. His drive and working knowledge of the process played a great part in the company's success.

Mr F. E. Frith hired the Parish Room in Old Town (now the British Legion Headquarters) for Mr Russell's retirement party. Messrs Stokes and Sons did the catering, which was still restricted by wartime regulations following the war and allowed only for sandwiches, cakes and tea. Speeches were made by Mr C. A. Boddington of the Berkshire Printing Company and Mr F. E. Frith. Mr William Smith, a local builder who was undertaking work for the company, did sketches and played the ukulele.

Unfortunately, he had a very short retirement, dying within two years. The funeral service was held in Charfield Chapel where a large number of the staff gathered to pay their last respects.

Post-War Developments

A shorter working week had been adopted during the war. The hours were cut from 50 to 45 hours, which meant a five-day working week.

Various improvements were carried out to help better production; one being a controlled humidity system for the machine room. Previously, the right conditions had to be made by the printers themselves.

Getting the right fuel for the boiler presented a problem. As previously mentioned, coke breeze had been used over the years but was now unobtainable. Loads of logs were bought but that only helped for a while.

Eventually the boiler was fired by gas, which, although expensive, proved highly efficient.

There had always been a problem of vibration, especially when the guillotine was being operated. More space was also needed, so a single-storey wooden building was erected on the left-hand side of the roadway at right angles to the main building. It was painted grey and had two entrances, one on to the drive furthest from the mill and the other was through the annexe (see plan, appendix 10).

This building housed the guillotine and two letter-presses. On the other side was the typesetting and two more small printing presses. Two or three tables were used for finishing the work, such as inspection, spotting and tissue interleaving, prior to guillotining.

The packing department was at the end of this building and furthest from the mill. Here a track and rollers were installed. These could be used for bulky packages, thus allowing them to be loaded through a small door directly on to the goods vehicle. This was useful when a number of large parcels was despatched.

The removal of the guillotine, spotting, finishing etc., from the first floor of the main building proved a great success.

The vibration from the guillotine was eliminated and the work from the presses could be taken on trollies to the letterpress and finishing departments in the long grey shed.

As this new building was on a higher level than the rest of the mill, a small lift was installed in the lobby from the annexe.

Retirement of Mr Charles Russell

About this time, 1947, Mr Charles Russell retired. He was born in London in 1879 and had two brothers, also collotype printers.

He came to Charfield to work for F. Frith & Co. by invitation of his brother, Harry, who had joined the company earlier. Both brothers had worked for Eyre & Spotteswoode in London.

During his many years with the company as a printer, whenever there was a slack period he was always willing to undertake routine maintenance. In those days no handyman was employed by the company so his help in this respect was much appreciated.

When the boiler needed descaling during a holiday period, he did this work, ready for the inspection.

On retirement he was presented with an electric fire by the staff.

Later, when the gravure factory was established at Charfield, he was employed in the gardens on a part-time basis. Always a hard worker, he finally finished when the gravure printing moved back to Wotton in 1960.

Further Building Changes

Part of the first floor vacated by the guillotine and packing was taken over as a negative filing department for postcards and publishing work. Special fire-proof metal cupboards were bought to store the negatives. These had been previously kept in the main outer office and in a wall safe.

To overcome an unreliable water supply, likely to be cut off without notice, a bore hole was sunk near the boiler house and an electric submersible pump fitted. Water always was a critical factor in making photographic negatives and also collotype plates. A softener and filtration plant was installed but with doubtful advantages.

As time went on and the supply of town water improved, mains water was eventually used throughout the factory.

With the removal of the guillotine and packing department from the first floor to the new shed, the need for the trap doors was considerably reduced. These had allowed the goods to be raised or lowered by a hoist installed on the top floor. The trap spaces were now shortened to allow a small enclosed lift to be installed.

This was a tremendous help, as for many years the glass plates had to be manhandled from the top to the bottom of the mill.

The trap doors were situated on the far right viewing from the front of the mill.

Besides the carrying of the collotype plates, the lift could be used for items up to one cwt. It was manually controlled by pulling on the thick rope operating the pulleys to raise or lower the goods.

Still more space was required, so another wooden building was erected on the other side of the drive, afterwards known as the green shed. Halfway down this building a porch was made and the checking-in clock was removed from the lobby on the first floor of the mill by the main office.

The part of the shed furthest from the mill was used firstly as a paper store.

Entrance to the mill from then onwards was through the porchway to the main press shop by the boiler house. A wider staircase having been put in recently to the first floor. The old one was so narrow that two people could only pass with great difficulty. From then on the stone steps were only used by office staff and visitors.

Better Conditions of Employment

A bonus scheme was introduced by the company which was welcomed by the staff. Fourteen days' paid holiday were given in July and a week's pay at Christmas.

Boiler fired by gas – late 1940s.

Grey shed erected *c*. 1947.

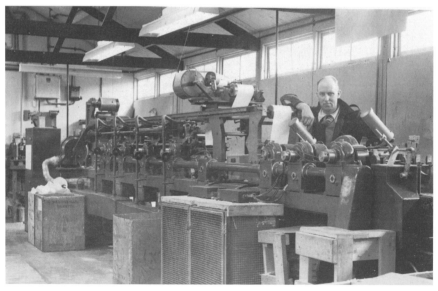

First gravure machine erected in the green shed – 1952.

Stanley Cole preparing a collotype plate for printing.

Cricket team, mid-1950s. Back row, left to right: Mr Mann (umpire), L. Smith, W. Durn, R. Brain, M. Hughes, S. Cole, D. Emes (author), D. Hollister (umpire). Front row: P. Neale, B. Candy, G. Bleaken, M. Cole, R. Hewish.

Exposing the collotype plates to daylight.

Two collotype presses in the annexe.

Gilbert Underhill coating a collotype plate prior to rolling it into the heated box.

Frederick Smart and Michael Cole turning a frame ready for the exposing room.

Firm outing to Ilfracombe – 1958. Boarding the gangway, left to right: H. Maunders, L. Cullimore, E. Cullimore, M. Cullimore, L. Smith, P. Smith, D. Smith.

Firm outing to London – 1962.

More Processing Developments

Several small colour jobs were undertaken, mostly supplied by Brooke Bond. Work from Frost & Reed was also beginning to arrive.

The boxes for the drying of the collotype plates after coating were converted from steam heating to electric tubular heaters thermostatically controlled.

Another improvement to the platemaking department was the transfer of the coated gelatin plates to the drying boxes on ball and socket supports. The plates were coated in the centre of the room where the plate table ran on a track.

The plate was level and at the same height as the ball and socket supports in the eight heated boxes. As the plate was coated by hand, it was slid over the ball supports into the boxes which ensured it remained perfectly level.

There were two coating rooms running the length of the north-west end of the mill. The second coating room was not always used and contained four boxes.

The Gelatin Platemaking Process

Coating took place in the morning and the plates were left in the boxes until totally dry. After exposure and washing out they were stored in a cupboard. This needed an even temperature and at one time they were kept on the second floor near the stairs. Finally, provision was made in the press shop after the lift had been installed.

The gelatin used in making the plates was a very important factor. When one batch of gelatin was running out several samples would be requested from the manufacturers, Nelson Dale.

These were tested firstly for viscosity, surface tension and keeping qualities. Although the gelatin samples sent were supposed to be very close to that in use, trials very often proved otherwise, because it was taken from various animal bones, hoofs and horns from different countries and our use for it was exacting.

After the platemaker had made his assessment of the samples, he would make a plate. Sometimes at this stage the samples would be rejected and others asked for, stating why those sent were unsuitable for our use.

Once again this procedure would be repeated and if considered satisfactory, another plate made.

The job used on this plate would only be known to the platemaker so as to make sure the result was not biased by the printer's knowledge of a different gelatin. If the job was printed to standard, more plates would be made and the opinions of other printers sought. If this was satisfactory only then would a batch lasting a couple of years or so be ordered.

Virtually every change in gelatin required adjustments in the making and also the treatment of the plate on the press.

Gelatin came in packets of narrow crinkled sheets about 8″ x 4″, one pound in weight.

The behaviour of gelatin was very difficult to assess, not only in making collotype plates but in using photographic film. Daily use would train the camera operators to know the characteristics of an emulsion. If the film being used was considered good the batch number would be quoted to the manufacturer and the film reserved for us for quite a long time in cold store. We would then order small quantities at a time until the batch was exhausted. Then again, more batches would be tested to find a suitable replacement.

The boxes of photographic film were kept in a cupboard on the second floor (retouching department). Bulk gelatin was also stored on this floor in a large crate.

Just before 8 a.m. one morning, as the staff were arriving for work, a young member of the company was cycling down the drive. On applying his brakes they failed to work and he ran into the mill just below a window. The force of the impact threw him through the window smashing the glass. Inside, a girl was preparing the press for work but seeing this young man flying through the window caused her to faint. She was off work for a week but the young man fortunately was not seriously injured and was able to return to work in a couple of days.

Into the 1950s: New Improvements – New Types of Work

As already mentioned, the heating of the mill was proving a problem so a Bristol firm of heating engineers was called in. They removed all the old steam heating system which had served the mill for many years. As the boiler was no longer required it was sold.

And Now Gravure

In 1952 the first moves were made towards the establishment of a gravure process when a suitable press was bought. This was erected in half of the green shed. Mr Harry Russell was keenly interested in printing labels by gravure. Like his father, he was always prepared to persevere with a new idea which would benefit the company.

Frank Wathen was the press operator working with Mr Russell. Many difficulties were met and gradually overcome as this was an entirely different printing method to collotype. Eventually they met with sufficient success for the press to be taken to Watsome Factory at Charfield, after Brooke Bond & Co. returned to their new works at Bristol.

This building had been used by Brooke Bond for tea packeting during the war and afterwards as a storage depot for spare parts for the red vans.

About this time Mr Harry Russell was appointed a Justice of the Peace, joining Mr Frith who had served from the early 1940s.

The Tea Connection Takes Off

The directors of the Berkshire Printing Co. always showed a keen interest in the collotype process and in the new venture of label printing. They were quick to help with advice and practical knowledge, and any equipment they had surplus and which could be used was readily available.

For a long time Mr K. G. Boddington came down from Reading for monthly meetings and it wasn't always a pleasant drive back in the winter! Sometimes Mr Neville Brooke came down to take a personal interest.

We also printed various pictures of tea production such as girls picking the leaves, manufacturing and packing the tea.

Part of the green shed was converted to a camera room housing a 40" x 40" camera. This was loaned to us from the BPC Reading. The other part of the shed, previously used by the gravure press, contained a varnishing machine and some paper was stored there. This machine coated the postcards with a spirit varnish and was dried with a series of infra-red heating lamps suspended over a continuous belt.

Prior to this, the postcards had been sprayed with a varnish coating in the covered area between the grey shed and the annexe.

A Larger Camera

A camera brought down from the Berkshire Printing Co. much earlier and temporarily housed in the darkroom area over the main office was removed. It was then re-erected on the second floor, thus giving ample space for working. This allowed a photographic printing room to be built in its place.

But Collotype Is Still in Demand

We were still printing a lot of postcards but the public needed a change from black and white and sepia, so a coloured card was introduced called collo-colour. Here are the details of working:

Stage 1
The normal edition of black (sepia) prints was taken from a standard (glass) plate.

Stage 2
A lighter print was taken from the same plate on a sheet of 115grm paper. This was then hand coloured using photo tints in the three basic colours.

Stage 3
A collotype *glass* plate was then made for the three colours to be used – yellow, brown/red and blue.

Stage 4
Each of the three (colour) plates were then in turn flooded with the usual water and glycerin (as in the normal print stage), so that the image in the plate would show the relief pattern of each illustration. To make this image easier to see, when on the light table, some neutral grey dye was added to the water-glycerin mixture.

After the relief image had been achieved the surplus water-glycerin was removed with a sponge and retained for future use. The surface moisture was then removed with thin paper (as used in the print stage).

Stage 5
A mixture of water and potassium bichromate was then painted on to the plate with a water colour brush on each area that included any yellow. After each illustration was painted it was dried by using blotting paper to remove excess bichromate. If mistakes were made, or any area was over painted it was permissable to cover these areas with Photopake (a dark red paint which held back the light). In order to achieve various densities of yellow, it was possible to airbrush Process Black over the individual areas in degrees of density to vary the weight of ink.

The same procedure was used for the brown/red and blue printers.

As an additional extra, the blue printer had clouds airbrushed on to the bichromate skies, using the Process Black.

The whole operation was carried out in darkened surroundings, on a light table to stop the bichromate hardening too quickly.

Stage 6
The plate was then exposed to daylight in order to harden the bichromate which had been painted on to the plate. This was then processed as a normal plate in the tank to wash out the bichromate, then dried ready for the printer.

The hand coloured thin prints were filed for future reprints.

This complete process (except the airbrushing of skies by the retouchers), was executed by a team of girls under the supervision of John Frith who devised the method. It was carried out on the first floor near the entrance to the main office. A large number of sheets were printed over the years. One sheet was a week's work for a press. Two days for the sepia base and one day for each of the three colours.

A sheet was made up of 36 postcard illustrations with a normal run edition of 1,000 copies giving an outrun of 36,000 postcards.

New Important Commissions

The work coming into the factory in the 1950s was of a greater variety.

Table mat prints were printed for 'Lady Clare' of Lutterworth. This type of work was undertaken for a long time. British Museum work was being printed and also work from overseas such as the Geological Survey of Australia and Palaeontology, etc.

One well-remembered picture we reproduced was called *La Route* by Vlaminck. This had been produced by use of palette knives and glass plates were used for the negatives. As the special effect of the surface of the painting had to be retained, high powered spot lights were needed. Fortunately, the BPC kindly supplied these.

We were receiving sheets of plaster casts of coins; this was our first experience of this type of work. Special lighting techniques had to be used to record the detail in the casts.

The printers also had to use great care in printing. Any blemish on the coins would mean another plate having to be made. Numismatists studied each collotype reproduction of the casts under a powerful magnifying glass to verify a true reproduction. This is why collotype suited this type of work admirably.

Ten sheets of the Dead Sea Scrolls for the Hebrew University were printed about this time. This was a 2,000 run job.

Management Changes

Mr Philip Brooke joined the Berkshire Printing Co. Reading in 1951, gaining experience in many departments.

He moved to the Cotswold Publishing Co. in 1955 having spent about a year with a foot in both camps. He spent time in retouching, platemaking and printing departments, and gave backing to Mr Frith on sales and Mr Russell on planning.

He was appointed managing director in 1959 and held this post until the business was sold and moved to Nailsworth.

Getting the Work Around

The gravure work was building up at Charfield and Mr H. Russell spent much time there, travelling in the Brooke Bond red van known as the 'scarlet runner'.

This van was used for many purposes, such as the transportation of materials to outworkers for the making of catering-size tea bags. These had to be assembled carefully with a greaseproof lining.

I witnessed a strange incident involving this van. It was parked on the roadway between the two sheds and a little way behind it on its stand was a BSA motorcycle.

The driver came from the packing department, got in the van and proceeded to reverse steadily, at the same time pushing the motorcycle a few yards on its stand. No damage was done to the van or motorcycle, which still remained upright.

Mr Frith scorned the use of mechanical transport and rode his bicycle quite often when attending the Magistrates Court as a Justice of the Peace. He could be seen daily riding to work from his house at the top of Haw Street. On the front of the cycle was fixed a basket in which he carried an attaché case for collecting the wages from the Bank. It would be a very risky thing to do these days!

A New Name – the Cotswold Collotype Co. Ltd.

In 1955 it was decided to change the name of the company from The Cotswold Publishing Company to the Cotswold Collotype Co. Ltd. This more aptly described the nature of the printing undertaken.

But First a Look in the Mirror

The renaming of the process reminds me of the mid-1930s. The naming of some of the cards was called Collogravure, likening it to a more modern printing process, namely photogravure.

Collotype was never an easy process to print and those printing it had to be dedicated.

Two plates rarely worked the same and the press room was influenced by outside conditions. The humidity which each printer required varied and that could cause problems. Not until the Berkshire Printing Co. acquired the company and put in a humidity system was this condition eased.

Postcard printing, which was an important feature, could prove to be very difficult.

The sheets contained thirty-six subjects and some could be quite varied. Most were a mixture of old and new negatives. In the early days these were made by daylight which could be very variable, giving negatives of unequal densities.

Many of the subjects making a sheet consisted of negatives ten and twenty years old and this always caused problems. When stored the negatives increased in density and contrast. Often these had to be worked on the press with a certain number of new negatives. It took a printer some time to work up the plate, besides the difficulties just mentioned, as the subjects differed greatly.

Some could be light seaside views, others were street scenes with heavy shadows.

Whatever work a printer did to his plate, there was always the tendency for it to revert to the original condition. This meant constant vigilance.

Each job required different treatment. Publishing work, for instance, could be made up of a variety of subjects, but usually not more than a dozen to twenty on a sheet.

A postcard which sold well and of which many sheets were printed was called Ambertone. The sheets were run through the press firstly with a sepia ink then a second time using an underexposed plate, printing mostly shadows, using a darker ink. This gave the card a greater depth of colour.

Brooke Bond Staff Award Scheme and Benefits

In 1956 Brooke Bond included the company in their long-service awards. This was a very generous gesture as some of the staff had served quite a number of years with the Cotswold Publishing Co. before it was acquired by the Brooke Bond Group.

These presentations took place at Reading, the qualifying period having been reduced to thirty years. Awards could be chosen from gold watches or mantel clocks and were indeed very nice presents. The first of the staff to receive the gifts were Mr F. E. Frith and Mr H. Russell, directors, Mr Jack Goscombe, works manager, Miss Phyllis Wyatt, Mr William White and Mr Gilbert Underhill. Further presentations took place in London (a short account is included of a later presentation).

A further generous gesture was made in 1970. The qualifying time was reduced to twenty-five years, and for those who had served forty years there was a gift of £100 to be spent on a suitable present. That meant several of us received a gold watch *and* the £100!

Most of the staff wanted to join a hospital scheme (WPA) so those wishing to partake could have the contributions deducted from their wages.

Nearly everyone took advantage of this easy method of payment.

Research and Academic Connections

From time to time a number of technical students from the printing colleges at Gloucester and other cities visited the works. Most seemed very interested, it being a process they had read about but never seen practised. Occasionally, the Master Printers would organise a trip to see the unusual process. About twice a year a Palaeontographical Society would make a visit to see their own prints being produced for the journals.

These geologists travelled from all over the country and usually ended up at the Falcon Hotel for lunch. Here they could discuss their geological finds. Some collected from quarries on the way to Wotton.

Staff and Workforce Changes

Following the trend in industry, the working week was reduced from forty hours to thirty-seven and a half, which seriously reduced the output. However, a man was employed to come in at 5.30 p.m. solely to 'wash up' the presses which enabled printing to continue right up to that time.

Retirement of Mr Frank Russell

On 8 March 1957, Mr Frank Russell retired at the age of seventy-three, having been with the company for thirty-three years. He was the first to benefit under the Pension Scheme.

Frank began working at Charfield in the late 1890s when the business belonged to F. Frith & Co.

As an improver he went to Bristol and London but returned when the company moved to Wotton as the Cotswold Publishing Co. He worked in munitions during the 1914–18 war and emigrated to America in the early 1920s. In 1930 he came back to this country to work for the company once again as a printer.

In 1940 he was drafted into the aircraft industry, returning to the company at the end of hostilities.

A craftsman of the old school, he had no time for shoddy work. He was greatly missed by all.

Mr Frith made a presentation of a cut glass vase containing flowers on behalf of the staff.

Outings and Social Events

The company gave us all a day's outing for a number of years. I well remember some of them, such as the Isle of Wight, Porthcawl and Ilfracombe.

On this particular trip the weather was ideal and we started from Hotwells, Bristol on the paddle steamer *Balmoral*. The journey to and from Bristol was by coach.

These outings were finally dropped due, perhaps, to the increase in car ownership. People could choose to travel as and when they liked. To take its place, a Christmas Dinner and Dance was provided.

Various places were used, such as hotels at Berkeley, Cirencester and Restaurant 77 (Wotton). In later years, the Cotswold Edge Golf Club was chosen. To these dinners the pensioners and their wives were invited and also given a voucher to be spent in the New Year.

The Impact of Colour

The Collocolour cards had now been running for several years and we were printing them for a number of firms. The demand for the monochrome cards we had printed throughout the life of the company was decreasing. The public wanted colour and this was apparent in their own family photos. Black and white snapshots became almost non-existent.

Camera Problems Temporarily Solved

Towards the end of the 1950s the Berkshire Printing Co. needed the large 40″ x 40″ camera they had loaned us. This was returned and any large negatives had to be made elsewhere for the time being. A camera this size wasn't readily available.

Thanks to the efforts of Mr Philip Brooke, Pitman's of Bath allowed us to use their camera on occasions. We also used the large one at Haycock Press, Ladbrooke Grove, London and one owned by Mardon Son & Hall, Bristol.

We reproduced a painting called *Elephant Celebes* on this occasion with the help of Mr Norman Hardesty, who previously worked at Mardons, and we secured permission to use their camera. Norman worked for our company for several years before retiring. (As mentioned earlier, he came during the war to supervise the printing of *Pines on the Dunes* and *Lady with the Harp* on behalf of Robinsons, Bristol.)

New Factory Is Built

Soon a new factory would have to be built to house the gravure section of the business. Journeys had constantly to be made backwards and forwards to Charfield, and more suitable premises were needed close at hand.

Fortunately, the directors were able to acquire a site across a footpath from Britannia Mill. This had been a garden and orchard belonging to the house where Mr Frith lived before moving to Haw Street. At that time the orchard and house belonged to Mr Sidney Isaac.

The factory took about a year to build and contained the cylinder making department and engineering workshops moved from Reading. There were also ink stores, a canteen and offices.

Death of Mr R. Cecil

We were shocked by the sudden death of Mr R. Cecil in 1959. He had come to manage the Brooke Bond factory at Charfield in the early days of the war. If we needed advice or any help, he was always willing to come to our aid.

Friths Still Going Well

Friths of Reigate had had a good year and was still being run by the Sargent brothers, Frederick and Trevor. They had been co-directors since 1945. Much earlier, in 1939, Mr Eustace Frith had died and the business sold to Mr A. F. Sargent. He had previously worked for Lilywhites and Raphael Tuck Ltd., both in connection with postcard view production.

Fifty Years On

Postcard work continued to be the bread and butter work of our company. Many more interesting jobs were printed but the profit margin on them was not very high. (A sheet of postcards contained 36 subjects 5½″ x 3½″ and later this number was increased to 42, and that is quantity as well as quality.)

In 1959 there were seventy people employed in collotype including three people in the office. The gravure section employed another sixteen.

On 24 April 1959 the company paid a record £101 in overtime!

During the last few years we had been printing quite a number of coin jobs and making a success of them. We were also producing a number of small colour jobs.

We Celebrate

On 5 May 1959 we celebrated the company's fiftieth year with a Jubilee Dinner and Dance. Eighty-eight staff, and one hundred and twenty people altogether, attended the dinner and many more the dance.

This very successful celebration was organised by Mr Philip Brooke, necessitating several visits to London. He was also instrumental in getting the Jubilee booklet printed.

Some of the Brooke Bond directors were there and all those from the Berkshire Printing Co. Ltd.

Mr John Brooke, chairman of the parent company, and Mr K. G. Boddington gave speeches. Tom Sims was toast master and Frank Wathen received his gold watch for long service from the Chairman.

It was a beautiful evening and while the tables were being cleared for the dance, drinks were served in the Swan Hotel.

The dance was very well attended, wives and friends having been invited, and it was a very successful evening.

To Strike or Not to Strike?

Sadly, we have to report that soon after this happy occasion, we were affected by the ripples (or was it a tidal wave?) of industrial unrest in the printing industry nationwide. Strike action by major unions was being called and up and down the country many printing works were idle.

Most members of the company were rather upset about the situation, especially Mr Frith. The general feeling among most of our workers was that there was little option in the circumstances but to join in the industrial action.

Not all the unions gave instructions to strike and so members generally followed the advice of their particular unions. Those allowed to come in did so and did what they could until we could operate normally, the company making sure there was no loss of wages. The Brookeside factory was unaffected and continued printing throughout the strike. It was a great relief to everyone when it was all over.

Retirement of Mr F. E. Frith JP

Mr F. E. Frith retired on 3 June 1959. He had been a keen member of the Food Production Club during the Second World War. For a number of years he was chairman of the Board of Governors of the KLBG school and was a very hard working member of the British Legion. In 1942 he was appointed a Justice of the Peace to serve the Wotton Bench.

A radiogram was presented to him by Gilbert Underhill on behalf of all the staff. Mrs Frith was presented with a bouquet of flowers. Mr Harry Russell made a charming speech, and did not forget to mention Mrs Frith.

As it was a lovely summer day the presentation took place in front of the mill. Victor Jellings produced a beautifully lettered and illuminated address and scroll on parchment with all ninety names of the staff employed.

In the evening there was a dinner at the Swan Hotel at which all directors were present. The four pensioners, Mr Charles Beale, Mr Charles Russell, Mr Frank Russell and Mr Jim Mabon, were also present. Mr Cope came from the London office and Mr Keith Boddington and Mr Reg Ballard came from Reading.

At the end of the evening, Mr and Mrs Frith were driven to their new home at Grist Cottage, Coombe Lakes. This newly acquired bungalow suited them admirably – beautiful surroundings, no noisy traffic, a large garden, and a lovely lake with trout fishing nearby.

Jubilee dinner – 1959.

Mrs H. Russell
Mr W. Childs
Mrs Cope
Mr P. Brooke
F. Wathen
Mrs Wathen
L.S. Smith
P. Barton
M. Davis
L. Smith
C. Russell
L. Nicholls
R. Chappell
R. Dancox

L. Cullimore
S. Birt
D. Merrett
H. Butcher
R. Alway
J. Warrell
C. Foxwell
M. Birt
E. Goodfield
J. Beale
V. Jellings
J. Morgan
B. Lawrence
J. Stevens

Mr Cope
Mrs Childs
Mr D. Brooke
Mrs J. Brooke
Mr F. Frith
Mrs K. Boddington
Mr J. Brooke
Mrs F. Frith
Mr K. Boddington
Mrs N. Brooke
Mr H. Russell
Mrs R. Ballard

J. Portlock
M. Cole
H. Hurcombe
B. Candy
C. Evans
J. Price
A. Shellard
S. Cole
A. Martin
J. Mabbett
S. Robson
P. Neal
V. Walker
J. Stevens
F. Smart

F. Russell
W. Durn
P. Wyatt
H. Maunders
Y. Mundy
E. Peglar
W. Hayward
B. Fryer
L. Pearce
D. Emes (taking photo)
M. Clarke
A. Moreman
J. Dix
R. Hardy
R. Diment

G. Underhill
C. Beale
H. Mabon
M. Crew
P. Sharpe
R. Hewish
R. Evans
G. Bleaken
P. Fry
R. Brain
J. Cullimore
M.Hughes
M. Wilkins
O. Mabon
J. Hurcombe

Mr N. Brooke
Mrs P. Brooke
Mr R. Ballard
Mr D. Boddington
J. Goscombe
W. White
J. Glenny
J. Jeffrey
P. Smith
G. Smith
C. Timbrell
R. Woodward
E. Eacott
J. Mabon
L. Cross

(See also pp. 60 and 61)

Jubilee dinner.

Jubilee dinner.

Jubilee dinner dance.

Jubilee dinner. Left to right: Mrs N. Brooke, Mr K. Boddington, Mrs F.E. Frith, Mr J. Brooke.

Jubilee dinner. Left to right: Christine Evans, Jennifer Dix, Pamela Smith, Rose Evans.

Jubilee dinner. Left to right: Mr S. Cole, Mr M. Hughes, Mr D. Merrett, Mr K. Boddington, Mr Childs, Mr E. Goodfield, Mrs F.E. Frith, Mr F.E. Frith

Presentation to Mr F.E. Frith on his retirement – June 1959.

Directors and the Law

Mr F. E. Frith and Mr Harry Russell Jnr. had been JPs on the same Bench but both resigned from the Magistracy in 1960 when Wotton-under-Edge Petty Sessional Division ceased to operate, and the functions and area of jurisdiction were transferred to Dursley. Mr Frith had been retired a year when this took place.

New Management and Administration

Mr Philip Brooke was appointed managing director, and Mr Lawford Smith became printing shop overseer. About this time the new building of Brookeside had been completed and was working. Some of the administration was still being undertaken in the offices on the first floor of the mill. Also on that floor negatives were filed in large fireproof metal safes. Any jobs which came in and needed negatives previously used were sorted there.

In the Money Business

The coin illustration work had steadily built up over the years. We were regularly printing the illustrations for the Numismatic Journal and Chronicles, also Glendenning, Carson Christie Manson & Woods, Blunt, Sylloge of British Coins, Spink, English, Ancient and Foreign, Bloech, Glasgow University, Sotheby Coin Sales and others.

Plaster casts were usually supplied for us to make negatives – these gave a better result than the actual coins. There were no reflections to worry about and the casts were of a uniform colour.

Our Own Really Big Camera at Last

A new 20″ x 20″ camera was bought from Pictorial Machinery Ltd. and was installed on the second floor. The previous camera had been used by us for twenty years, and much longer by the Berkshire Printing Company who installed it.

This new camera was necessary to cope with the greater variety of work undertaken by the company. Special backs were made for the camera, so that 8½″ x 6½″, 10″ x 8″ and 12″ x 10″ film slides could be used, making for speedier operation.

These were very useful as different jobs varying in size could be dealt with by changing the backs and using the appropriate size of slide very quickly.

'Lady Clare' of Lutterworth supplied many sheets of prints for table mats for us to print. These were hand coloured and made into mats, then heat-proofed by their own company.

Into the Academic Scene – The Dead Sea Scrolls

We were indeed fortunate in obtaining the printing of illustrations for the book *The Finds from the Bar Kochba Period in the Cave of Letters* by Yigael Yadin (The Hebrew University, published 1963). There were eighteen sheets backed (A&B) 1,500 + 1,500 copies printed. This was indeed a large order for the collotype process, and, without question, one of the company's most prestigious orders.

Mr Frith, together with Prof. Yadin, worked on the complicated details of reproduction. On the retirement of Mr Frith in 1959, Mr Philip Brooke continued the work with Prof. Yadin's son. It was printed with the generous support of Mr Charles Clore of London.

Lord Marks put at Prof. Yadin's disposal the photographic laboratories of Marks and Spencer Limited, should they be needed. The photographs of the papyri were of a very high standard.

The originals had been found in tall clay jars with lids in the caves at Qumran. These are now housed in The Shrine of the Book in the Israel Museum at Jerusalem.

This building is of a shape which itself reflects the shape of the clay jars in which the 1st Century BC scrolls had been preserved. In it the papyrus scrolls are exhibited and very securely guarded in a circular glass structure within the building. That circular glass structure can be lowered very quickly into the ground in the event of danger. Having been associated with the printing of this very important work, I was pleased later to have the opportunity of visiting the museum and Qumran when my wife and I paid a visit to the Holy Land.

Personal Awards – A Lovely Time to Remember

I promised to give a more detailed description of the long service awards. Stanley Davis and I, together with our wives, were included in the thirty years' service presentation.

Both of us had met our wives in the 1930s while working for the company. Stanley and Ethel worked in the letterpress department and Betty, my wife, worked with Mr Frith as his secretary when I was a camera operator.

On 10 June 1960 we went by train from Stroud to Paddington where we joined a party and were taken to our respective hotels. Ours was the Waldorf where lunch was provided.

Afterwards we were taken to the Brooke Bond head office in Cannon Street, shown around the main office and provided with light refreshments. A short tour of the city was included on the return journey to our hotels.

In the evening we met at the Connaught Rooms for the presentation dinner. Presentations were made at the tables by the late Mr John Brooke, who incidentally received his own gold watch on this occasion.

After dinner, we were entertained by Cy Grant, Ming Chow, Marion Ryan and John Pertwee at a cabaret.

This pleasant evening went very quickly indeed and about midnight we were taken to our hotel.

Next morning, after breakfast, we visited St Clement Danes Church, which was near our hotel and within walking distance. Then we were taken to Paddington Station and caught the train home. Our small party felt the arrangements made for us on this memorable occasion were excellent.

Retirement of Bill White

1960 saw the retirement of William White, known by his workmates as Bill. He joined the company before the 1914–18 war, when he went to France with the Gloucester Regiment. While serving there he met Harry Russell Jnr., son of one of the original directors. Returning to the company at the cessation of hostilities, he worked on the guillotine in the packing department.

At the outbreak of the Second World War in 1939 he was transferred to the Brooke Bond tea packing factory at Watsome, Charfield.

He always worked at a uniform pace and refused to be rushed. Of an inventive mind, he often made gadgets to help the flow of work. Once, being plagued with mice which seemed to dodge the orthodox methods of trapping, he made a self-setting trap of his own design.

This consisted of a narrow strip of wood finely balanced over a container of water. On the end of which was attached a piece of cheese. When the mouse negotiated the strip of wood, before reaching the cheese, it would suddenly dip, throwing the mouse into the water. The strip of wood would then return to its original position to await the next victim.

Mr Philip Brooke made a retirement presentation to him of a radio on behalf of the staff. Miss Phyllis Wyatt presented Mrs. White with a bouquet of flowers. These presentations took place in the newly opened Brookeside factory.

In Wotton's Industrial Exhibition, 1962

An exhibition was held in the Wotton Town Hall with a number of local industries displaying goods manufactured by them.

Our company joined this venture and erected several folding screens exhibiting a variety of printing. This included coins, table mats, palaeontology and reproductions of paintings.

The Range of Work Continues to Widen

We were still printing postcards but in a declining number, being chiefly for Friths, Millar and Lang, Valentines and a few others. More colour reproduction work and pictures were undertaken. For several years we had printed our own calendar.

We were delighted to receive a number of pencil drawings of superb quality from Sir William Russell Flint. Among them were *The Birth of Aphrodite*. He also wanted reproduced in colour two small pictures called *The Lisping Goddess*. This artwork was ideally suited for collotype and the printing was a great success. Single reproductions of the monochromes sold at £80 each.

About this time we also printed a picture called *Baby in the Red Chair* and *Jahili Fort* by Terrance Cuneo.

The negatives of a picture called *Elephant Celebes* by Max Ernst were made at Mardon Son & Hall, Bristol as we had no large camera at that time. The size to which we had to reproduce this painting was 32'" x 25" and was for Unicef.

Other reproductions were made from *The Queen at Sandhurst*, *Canadian Pacific Liner* and *Aircraft for the People*.

'Auntie Phyl'

In 1962 the retirement of Miss Phyllis Wyatt took place. She joined the company in the very early days, soon after the move to Wotton in 1912. She worked for many years on Mr Charles Beale's press and was finally in charge of the finishing department. Here she was affectionately known as 'Auntie'.

Always a good worker she ensured high standards were maintained by the girls in her charge.

Mr Harry Russell presented her with a clock on behalf of the staff. June Cullimore also made a presentation of a bouquet of flowers.

Taking a Slice of Waterlows

The firm of Waterlow of Dunstable was closing down their collotype department and knowing we were in the same line of printing, they contacted the directors. They were able to offer us two presses and camera equipment. Some of their printers were willing to come and finally Mr Leonard Latham and Mr Charles Howarth were prepared to move. Both were colour printers and had printed very little monochrome work. A number of sets of colour negatives were also available, all on glass plates, which hadn't been used for a number of years.

Both printers fitted in well with our own staff and stayed with the company until their retirement. Leonard then moved to Torquay and Charles continued living at Uley.

The American Connection and Into Rotary Collotype

One of the greatest advances made by the company was early in 1963. The BPC planned for Mr Philip Brooke to attend the Gravure Printing Convention in Chicago and to stop in New York to meet Mr Lewin, a friend of Mr Keith Boddington.

Within a few minutes, Mr Lewin had arranged for a meeting with one Mr Harry Lerner who ran a rotary collotype company in New York. Then began one of the greatest advances made by the company.

With the whole-hearted co-operation of the Berkshire directors and staff at Wotton great progress was made in the acquisition of the rotary method.

All essential information was obtained and Mr Lerner agreed to visit us when we had set up the equipment and made a start on printing.

In February 1963 Mr Harry Russell and Mr Lawford Smith visited Triton Press, New York. Their brief visit was to observe the details of the practical side of the process, both having had great experience in collotype printing and platemaking.

They were greatly impressed by what they saw. On their return, preparations were immediately put in hand to adopt rotary collotype.

Rotary Production and Process

A press was obtained and after a number of modifications it was suitable for printing. Lawford ran the press, passing his knowledge to the late Brian Candy who finally took over. This allowed Lawford to return to Production Control.

A printing room had been made under the original offices.

The setting up of a whirler for coating the plates and exposing lights etc. were housed in part of the green shed. This work was undertaken with the instructions of Mr H. Russell, who eventually passed on all the information regarding platemaking to Mr David Hopkins, who was in charge of that department.

Various other methods connected with the process were learnt, such as using an absorbent sheet of paper to dry the plate on the press and setting up the negatives for printing on sheets of 'golden rod' paper.

The negatives had to be made to a more exact standard, as the working up of the flexible collotype plate on the cylinder was difficult.

It was hoped the introduction of rotary collotype, with the much faster production of the collotype plate, plus the greater number of runs per day, would help forestall screenless litho as a competitor.

1963 Was Cold!

The early months of 1963 were very cold and the stream running by the mill was frozen over. I never remembered this happening before.

It meant a larger number staying for lunch owing to the difficult road conditions. A toboggan was brought by someone and, as the field by the side of the mill sloped quite a lot, we enjoyed the winter sport.

It could be hazardous too, remembering the stream at the bottom; although covered with ice it wouldn't stand much weight. Imagine our surprise when who should turn up on the slopes but Mr Brooke complete with skis!

We all watched and waited for what we thought was inevitable, but he didn't end up in the brook!

Retirement of Mr H. Russell JP

Mr Harry Russell saw the new venture of rotary printing started before his retirement in August 1963.

A presentation of a radiogram was made to him by Mr K. G. Boddington, managing director of the Berkshire Printing Company. Mrs Philip Brooke presented Mrs Russell with a bouquet of flowers. Also present were directors John and David Brooke.

He had been with the company the whole of his working life, chiefly as a printer until he became works director on his father's retirement. Having a wide knowledge of the process, he had helped at sometime or other in all departments connected with collotype. When the chance came to install a gravure machine he helped with the erection and running it in the green shed. Difficulties were met and overcome and there were many in the early days.

Success came eventually and after a while it was found necessary to move to the Charfield B.B. factory. Here there was plenty of space, although not ideal conditions. A few years later he directed the move back to Wotton to the new Brookeside factory. Like his father before him, he was very active in the worship at Charfield Congregational Chapel and his wife was organist, like his mother had been.

The Russell Line Continues in the Work

The family still has links with printing. Russell Alway, grandson of Charles Russell and great nephew of Mr H. J. Russell Snr., one of the original directors, is, at the time of writing, a gravure printer at the Berkshire Gravure Company and has been very helpful in supplying details of relatives who joined Friths at Charfield in the late 1890s.

Another link is through Mrs. Virginia Walton, great grand-daughter of Harry Russell Snr, who is a director and personnel officer with the Berkshire Printing Co. Reading. She supplied what information she could, as learnt from her grandmother.

Thus we have the Russell contribution to collotype, making a total of 180 years made up as follows:

Mr Harry J. Russell Snr.	50 years
Mr Charles Russell	50 years
Mr Frank Russell	35 years
Mr Harry Russell Jnr.	45 years

Mr Jack Goscombe Succeeds Mr Harry Russell

To fill the vacancy left by Mr Harry Russell, Mr Jack Goscombe was appointed works director. He had been works manager for a number of years having spent nearly all his working life connected with printing. During the First World War he joined the company as a collotype apprentice.

Mr Gilbert Underhill – Another Long-Service Technician

In November 1963 we were all saddened by the death of Mr Gilbert Underhill from a coronary thrombosis.

A large number of the staff attended the funeral but unfortunately Mr Lawford Smith and Mr Harry Russell were unable to attend owing to floods at Iron Acton.

Gilbert joined the company in 1920, having first been employed as a footman at Tortworth Court. He worked with Mr Bagwell in the platemaking department where he continued until his death.

On Mr Bagwell's retirement in the early 1930s he took charge of platemaking, working in close co-operation with Mr Frith, chiefly in the setting-up techniques needed in the production of book illustrations and furniture catalogues. Both were keen gardeners and both had a liking for Tom Thumb lettuce! For many years Mr Frith presented Gilbert with a packet of these seeds every spring.

Being a very conscientious person, he was of a worrying nature and was always concerned that high standards should be maintained in the platemaking.

His father owned the Coombe Valley Brewery which closed about 1910. By coincidence, on his retirement, Mr Frith chose a bungalow on this site which, to his delight, had a large garden.

One day, while Mr Frith was digging in the garden, he dug up two of the old-fashioned mineral water bottles; these were the type with a glass marble as a sealer, against a rubber ring in the neck. To Gilbert's great pleasure the bottles had the family name of Underhill cast in them. One was empty but the other contained mineral water which in those days was called lime juice and soda.

These bottles are still in the possession of his daughter, Mrs. Kathleen Downs.

1964–6 – More Building

In 1964 a decision had been made by the directors to enlarge the collotype business by erecting an addition to the main building. This was square in shape, brick built with a flat roof. Provision was made for the rotaries and platemaking with the guillotining, letterpress and paper store in the larger part of the building.

Mr Lawford Smith was also moved to Progress and Planning at this stage.

Any work previously carried out in the grey shed was to be continued in this new building. The grey shed had to be demolished for the new building and most of the work dealt with there was transferred temporarily to the Brookeside factory, which was not fully in use.

Two entrances were made, one into the annexe, the other through the loading bay on to the road.

Provision had been made for its own heating system, air conditioning and humidity control, all of which is an essential requirement of platemaking and printing. The building was finished in 1965.

A name was required for this new building so the company invited suggestions from the staff for a suitable one.

Finally, Trident was chosen and two members of the company (I was one) shared the prize (a trident being the three pronged spear in the hand of Britannia and this being the third factory). Britannia Mill, the main building, was the first, Brookeside the second and Trident the third.

Re-siting Equipment to Use New Floor Space

The new building was now completed. All presses and equipment were brought into the new factory from Brookeside, including the rotary platemaking which had temporarily used part of the green shed.

Then came the chance to acquire the 40″ x 40″ camera we had used at Haycock Press. It was purchased and erected in the green shed after the removal of the platemaking equipment. For a few years we were able to produce our largest negatives without going elsewhere.

Whilst Trident was being built, the camera room over the original offices was completely altered. This made way for two small cameras. The second one was needed as the company now employed an apprentice.

To get this work done, the large lobby at the entrance to the darkrooms was absorbed, leaving a narrow space for the existing sink to be available for general use.

When the rotary platemaking equipment had been installed in Trident, the staff was divided, leaving two to deal with the diminishing number of glass plates needed. The remaining staff were transferred to their new department in rotary with David Hopkins in charge.

Retirement of Mr Jack Goscombe

Mr Jack Goscombe retired in July 1966. He joined the company in 1916 during the First World War, working on the printing side most of his life. In his early days he spent time in the platemaking department with Mr Bagwell.

Company stand being prepared for Trade Exhibition in Town Hall – 1962.

Demolition of grey shed for Trident factory – 1964.

Foundations being dug for new factory.

Mr K. Boddington making a presentation of a radiogram to Mr H. Russell on his retirement – August 1963.

The new Trident factory almost completed – 1965.

Presentation of a radio to Mr Jack Goscombe by Mr Philip Brooke – July 1966.

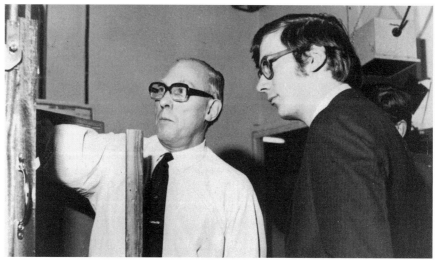

HRH Prince Richard being shown a large camera on his visit to the company – September 1971.

He was directed to Parnells in 1940 on essential war work, but was able to return to the company in 1942. This was to enable him to print colour work for the American market, as mentioned earlier, thus earning dollars.

On the retirement of Mr H. Russell he was promoted to works director, having been works manager for a number of years.

Mr Brooke made a presentation of a portable radio on behalf of the staff. As it was a nice day this took place in front of the mill, witnessed by most of the workers.

Some Operational Changes

Mr Lawrence Cullimore was appointed Flatbed Overseer. He had joined the company in the early 1930s and had worked as a collotype printer for many years gaining much valuable experience.

Mr Brian Candy was promoted overseer of the newly established rotary printing. He started with the company in the early 1940s and had worked as a printer since then. Unfortunately, he died in 1988 on holiday in Singapore where he had much earlier completed his National Service.

Rotary Collotype Platemaking

The procedure for making rotary plates was entirely different than flatbed.

Plates 18^{thou} thick were fastened in a whirler which would take up to a 60″ x 40″ plate, and were coated in a near vertical position. We were now following as closely as possible the method practised in the New York factory of Mr Harry Lerner.

The gelatin was mixed in 7 kilo amounts (obtained from Liners of Trefforest) and kept in solution at a controlled temperature before use. Freedom from dust and air bubbles was essential. Enclosed, the plate was whirled for twenty-five to thirty minutes at 120°F. The gelatin was now dry and an absolutely even surface of .0005 thick was obtained.

At this stage the plate was then stored until needed for printing when it was immersed in a solution of potassium bichromate to render the gelatin light sensitive. Until the plate was needed for the press, precise humidity and temperature were maintained. From then on, the plate was handled in much the same way as a litho plate.

The layout of the negatives was placed emulsion side down on the gelatin surface and the plate exposed to mercury vapour light for ten to fifteen minutes.

Then the bichromate was removed by washing in a tank at a controlled temperature. The plate was then stored for a short period only. Preparation began by immersing the plate in glycerin and water solution for about thirty minutes. It was then sponged over and clamped on to the plate cylinder of the printing press.

Apart from precise humidity and temperature control, the procedure was now similar to that followed in litho.

A much greater number of runs were obtained on the rotary presses, varying from 5,000 to 6,000 against 750 or so a day on flat bed.

Most work which could be produced on flat bed could be undertaken on rotary. Quite a number of sale catalogues for Sotheby's were printed besides coins and palaeontology subjects.

The presses had their separate rooms, for each printer to maintain the condition most suitable for the type of work he was printing. Two 60″ x 40″ and two 30″ x 40″ presses were erected and printers for these were taken from the flat bed.

As one would expect, after these four presses had been erected some troubles were bound to occur with totally different machines, a new method of printing in a new factory, and also a greater variety of work.

The printers coped well with these difficulties and after a while Mr Harry Lerner came over from America to gain an overall picture of the progress made in all departments of rotary printing.

Generally speaking, most of the colour work was produced on flat bed where the number ranged from a few hundred to a thousand.

Mr Cyril Wellings – Works Manager

Towards the end of 1966, Mr Cyril Wellings joined the company as works manager. He had previously been employed by Metal Box Ltd., Liverpool. He was responsible for both gravure and collotype production. His office was on the first floor of the mill and adjoining the main office of Mr Brooke.

Soon regular morning meetings were being held here from approximately nine to nine-thirty. Heads of departments attended. We were able to discuss jobs about to be undertaken and also to inform the meeting on the progress of work in hand. Ideas could be advanced and advice put forward to help production.

Mr Brooke would sometimes attend to gain first hand information and also put forward suggestions. Sometimes he would call a meeting, when necessary, in his own office. This was usually when something of an urgent nature needed discussing.

First Impressions

On the suggestion of Mr Cyril Wellings, a reception area was created adjoining Mr Brooke's office. This utilized what used to be a lobby and the checking in clock had been installed there previously.

This made a great improvement. Some pictures we had produced were attractively framed and hung. A receptionist had a desk and met visitors; a favourable impression was thus created on entering the factory.

Some Notes on Our Colour Work Commissions

At this stage, a few words can be written regarding some of the colour jobs undertaken.

These included the company's calendar, with a painting of Coombe Hill, Wotton by Mr Donald Milner as frontispiece (he had been president of the Royal Academy of Art in Bristol); *The Queen at Sandhurst* by Cuneo; *Canadian Pacific*; *Pacific Liner* and *Aircraft*; *End of the Grouse Season*; *Turkey Drive*; *Soldiers in Uniform*; *Cheetahs* by David Sheppard; and *Ex Libris. Barque Running Before a Storm* was printed on the rotary and numbered several thousand copies.

One of the unusual jobs we were asked to print were paper dresses for a magazine aiming at the sixteen to twenty-four age group and which were to form the basis of the publicity campaign; these were printed by the company on the rotary. A number of litho houses were approached but there was no possibility of this work being done by that process. These made eye-catching displays using the paper culotte dresses. The company received the order from Messrs.

Peter Callis, clothes merchants, using specially treated paper from the Reed group.

The printing took ten days to complete. Peter Callis then cut out the patterns and stitched the dresses together.

Another special job admirably suited for collotype were prints for the firm called Sackin. Mr Larry Sackin visited the mill unannounced. 'I've been everywhere and no one will undertake to print on this stuff,' he said, handing Mr Brooke a sheet of rice fibre paper. 'Can you print it?' he asked.

'I doubt it,' replied Mr Brooke, 'but let us go and try!'

So saying, both went downstairs and the overseer Mr Lawrence Cullimore was asked to put a sheet on a press to try. Some minor adjustments were made, the sheet laid on the feed board and an impression taken. To Mr Sackin's delight the printer peeled his sheet off the cylinder, handed it over and said, 'I think that will be all right.' Then followed many years of continuous orders for short run work.

Years later Mr Sackin said, 'I've never forgotten those words – "but let us go and try it".'

Quite a large variety of subjects was supplied for us to print. Among them were *Ballooning in the early days*, still life, views, world maps, hunting scenes, horse racing, *Battle of Trafalgar*, *Chess Table Tops*, *Oriental Drawings*, *Infantrymen*, *Signs of the Zodiac*, *British Army Officers*, Chinese scenes, views of London, *Spanish Riders*, *Partridge Shooting*, *Carriages*, patterns for sporting prints and Queen Elizabeth I portraits (etchings and engravings).

The prints our company supplied were stuck on the glass and when dry were painted from underneath the supported glass by artists, using the very transparent print as a guide. Apart from the printing, Sackin did all the other work. When framed, the front side of the glass was untouched, all the work having been done on the reverse side.

For a short time, silk screen work was undertaken, and some of Sackin's subjects suitable for this process were produced in the green shed.

A very nice job printed by the company was called *The Drawings of Fishes* from Captain Cook's Voyages (BMMH 1968 Publication No. 670 – Price £21) – forty drawings of fishes made by the artists who accompanied Captain James Cook on his three voyages to the Pacific from 1768 to 1771. Some were used by authors in the *Description of New Species* (text by P.J.P. Whitehead).

These drawings were very nicely produced. Some species of fish were painted in watercolours. In some instances, these drawings, when brought back to this country, were the first sight of what the seas held on the way to Australia.

The Blounts Court research laboratories from Reading, a subsidiary of Berkshire Printing Company, helped in overcoming some of the difficulties we were experiencing in rotary plate making. Additional equipment was obtained and a member of their staff joined the company.

Colin Stockwell was appointed sales executive for collotype. He contacted art galleries, museums and universities for the type of work we needed. In fact, he was the first sales representative the company employed and he soon became invaluable.

The pressure on the retouching department, having to opaque the negatives around the image of the coins to produce a clean background, was time consuming. Some pages contained over a hundred coin plaster casts which had to be carefully painted around to keep the exact shape.

The camera room, being aware of this time consuming job, devised a photographic method. The plaster casts had to be mounted on rigid clear perspex instead of card. These were fastened, a plate at a time, to a Kodak transparency Viewer. The method of copying the casts was, as usual, making the standard negative for printing.

Without altering the camera equipment in any way, a second negative was made by switching off the front lights used to illuminate the casts and switching on the Kodak Viewer. This illuminated the casts from the rear. Another negative was made using lith film (contrast film). The casts of the coins being made of plaster of Paris were opaque making masks for the coin negative.

The two negatives were bound together in perfect register producing the casts on an opaque background. This eliminated the tedious blocking out (painting around) of each coin by the retouching department and achieved freedom for more skilled work.

The End of the Frith Postcard Connection

In 1971 the printing of Friths postcards finished. This ended a long association with our company starting in 1907 when Friths sold the collotype business to three of their employees – Mr Russell, Mr

Bagwell and Mr Jeater. The latter two had been employed by Friths at Reigate before moving to Charfield.

The postcard work was then returned to Saxony for printing. From 1909 the company was renamed the Cotswold Publishing Co. Ltd.

Mr F.E. Frith, grandson of the founder of the photographic and postcard firm of Reigate, had joined our company in 1920 as a director and Friths cards were again printed in this country.

Over the years their postcard business built up and they became our best customer for postcards.

Allow me to re-cap on the Frith connection. In 1935 their large factory at Reigate had been sold and the business moved to Raglan Road. At the same time, Mr A.F. Sargent joined the company. He had been associated with the production of local views and had a wide experience in this direction.

Mr Eustace Frith died in 1939 and the business was sold to Mr Sargent.

After the war, the two sons, Frederick and Trevor, joined the company as managing directors of F. Frith & Co.

The post-war years saw a gradual decline in their postcard work and in 1968 the business was sold to Pandora. Both brothers stayed on as consultants but the company entered into voluntary liquidation.

This ended a fifty-year link with our company. We had printed more postcards for them than any other customer. Three Friths had found employment with the CCC – Mr F.E. Frith as a director, John, his son, for a number of years after the 1939–45 war, and Phoebe for a short time until she was old enough to join the WAAF.

Into the 1970s

The office staff was increased as the workload grew. This increased work consisted of the calculation and making up of the wages, etc., for the Brookeside factory.

The early 1970s also saw the end of the flat bed plate glass system. However, our market called for flat bed quality and for economic reasons we had to devise a new system.

The presses were adapted to take aluminium plates of a much thicker gauge than that used by rotary, but answering the same purpose. This speeded up the production much faster than glass and the platemaking could then be confined only to Trident.

The two remaining staff working with the glass platemaking were also transferred.

All the flat bed glass making equipment was removed from the top floor where it had been in use for nearly sixty years. This was a situation that could not have been visualised in the early days.

It was unfortunate the department was so far away from the press room for so many years.

A Royal Visit

In September 1971 a member of the Royal Family paid a secret visit to the company. This was His Royal Highness Richard, The Duke of Gloucester.

The following is an extract taken from the *Tea Flyer*:

> This visit was made to see the printing of illustrations photographed by him for a book called *On Public View*. The business visit was so secret that there were no banners or crowds to greet the Queen's first cousin.
>
> The Prince came to Stroud by train and thence by car to the factory. The book dealt with London sculptures, 114 of which will appear when the book is released in October.
>
> Following lunch at The Swan, the Prince who has a keen interest in history and architecture visited St. Mary's Parish Church at Wotton. He showed great interest in the Berkeley Brasses and the organ which was played by Handel.
>
> Until 1800 the organ was at St. Martin's in the Field, from where it was bought for £200 and transferred to Wotton.

We Need to Widen Our Net for More Commissions

In May 1972 the company invited suitable applications for the post of sales representative for our Collotype Company alone. He would be trained by Mr Colin Stockwell, who had been covering this as sales executive. Mr Glyn Jones, who had been a collotype printer for several years, was chosen. His knowledge of the type of work for the process was a great asset.

More Equipment Moves Around

Our 40" x 40" camera could now be removed from the green shed to the top floor of the main building vacated by the glass platemaking. This brought the camera department much closer together and saved time going to and fro. The sink was left and a new one built to our requirements to take four 40" x 30" dishes.

The negative filing department was also transferred together with the cabinets. The space left was used by the office staff on the first floor.

Sets of glass negatives of large pictures, together with samples were kept in what was previously the exposing room of the platemaking.

Our first job on the resited large camera was 'The Bristol Charter'. This was quite a large document and printed very well.

We were printing several colour jobs at this time, such as Nordon Maps, L.S. Lowry's *Ferry Boats*, and *The Harbour*.

Storms Loom Ahead – Production Speeds and Competition Face the Art Printer

In 1972 the staff were shocked by the following letter from the managing director, Mr Philip Brooke, to heads of departments:

> It must seem curious to many of you that having virtually overcome our production problems, we are obliged to announce quite serious redundancies.
>
> Looking back a number of years, we foresaw that glass plates on flat bed machines were losing ground, so we turned to the rotary presses and metal plates.
>
> We encountered what appeared to be insurmountable problems and while production was restricted and unpredictable, it followed that the sales value was low. We carried on hoping the situation would improve.
>
> With the help of Blounts Court Research team we are now able to forecast with reasonable accuracy the value of work we can produce each week.

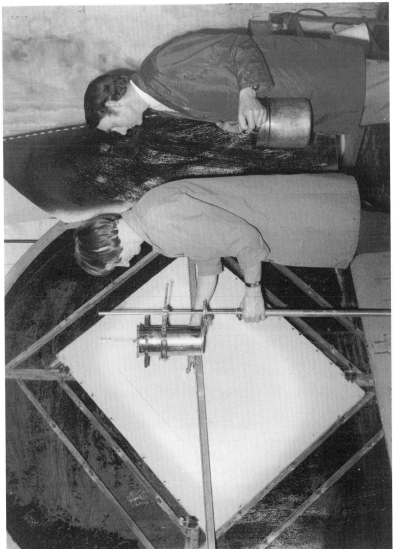

Douglas Easthope and Robert Brain coating a metal collotype plate in the whirler.

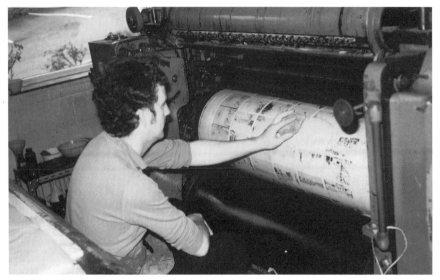

Godfrey Smith working on the R46 Press.

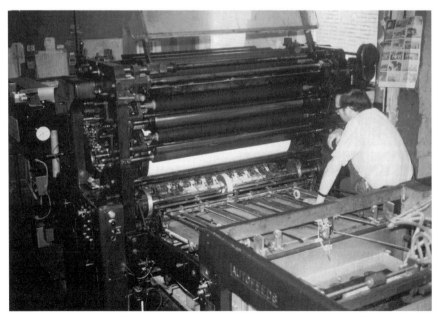

Brian Candy adjusting the Consul Press.

Rear of the 40″ x 40″ camera showing the vacuum back open.

The 60″ x 40″ frame for holding originals when 'copying'.

Derek Merrett working on the Consul Press.

Rear view of the Consul Press.

Measuring the gelatin thickness of a sensitised collotype metal plate.

Robert Marsh in the Testing Laboratory.

Exposing frame for rotary collotype.

Sir Humphrey Prideau, chairman of the Brooke Bond group, being shown around the Press Room by Mr Philip Brooke – 4 September 1976.

Victor Jellings correcting a Lowry negative.

At The Fleece, Hillesley, for the retirement of Mr L. Cullimore and the author – 1977. Back row, left to right: Mr L. Cullimore, Mr L. Smith, Mr P. Emes, Mr C. Wellings, Mr B. Candy. Front row, left to right: Mr P. Brooke, Mrs E. Cullimore, Mr D. Emes, Mrs B. Emes.

Last of the morning meetings in Mr Wellings's office. Left to right: Mr L. Cullimore, Mr C. Wellings, Mr B. Candy, Mr D. Emes (author), Mr V. Jellings, Mr R. Durham.

Remaining staff before closing – October 1980. J. Luker, P. Lottinga, H. Maunders, R. Hardy, D. Hopkins, T. Luker, V. Jellings, J. Sims, J. Pearce, J. Young, L. Smith, B. Candy, N. Todd, D. Taylor.

Improved techniques made in camera department, on colour correction and in retouching, closing down glass platemaking, colour work and postcards now being printed on the R46, are new factors leading to increased production and sales.

To produce is one thing – to attract is another, and balancing production cost with what we considered attainable in sales was not an easy problem. However, we looked at it, and it was clear that we had to reduce our costs in order to make the business profitable.

Your department managers have been fully informed all through this re-formation of our manpower. They have contributed much of value and we now consider this marks the beginning of a successful company.

For the first time ever we can view the future with confidence in the collotype process and much as the directors regret making redundancies, we believe the business is now perfectly capable of standing on its own feet and being profitable.

With your help we will achieve our goal.

Promise Cards

With the end of the Frith cards came also an abandonment of collocards, but in 1972 it was decided to print an improved card. Colour separation sets of negatives that were scanned for colour correction were to be used.

Mr Victor Jellings went to Trident, New York to study the method they used to produce this type of card. The origination was to be 35mm colour transparencies. These were obtained by advertisement and sets of six or more were accepted.

The name give to this coloured card the company were about to produce was 'Promise'. These cards continued to be produced for quite a while but not without difficulty, as quality was hard to maintain. After printing 100 sheets their production was discontinued in February 1975.

The closure of the collo-colour department made more room on the first floor for the office staff also Progress and Planning.

Mr K.G. Boddington retired from the Berkshire Printing Company in 1973, where he had been managing director for many years. For a long time after the war he had paid monthly visits to our company.

He showed a keen interest in collotype and went to America to see the rotary operating at Trident. No doubt his favourable comments on his return helped a great deal for the process to be installed at our company.

In his place, Mr K. Cotton was appointed as managing director of the Berkshire Printing Company.

Even More Specialist Art Work

As we were printing fewer postcards on flatbed, more artwork was being produced on these presses. We had previously printed several pictures by the artist L.S. Lowry and were accepting a few more, namely *The Church Steeple, Burford Church, Industrial Scene, Landscape* and *Sailing Boats*. A picture of *Buffle Headed Ducks* and *The Duke of Beaufort* were some jobs printed that year.

As the flatbed glass plates were finished we were totally committed to metal. However, the printers coped with this situation and problems were eventually overcome.

In the autumn of 1974 the following appeared in the *Brooke Bond Liebig International*:

> *Scarlet Macaw Parrot* printed by the CCC is among thirty unusual pieces of printing material on exhibition in the Design Centre, London.
>
> The collotype print in the exhibition was one of twenty which the CCC printed for a book on Chinese Natural History. The reproduced drawings were selected from the Reeves collection in the British Museum (Natural History). The Reeves collection is reckoned to be one of the greatest achievements in the collaboration between European and Chinese Artists, numbering as it does over 2,000 animal and plant drawings. These rank as some of the finest examples of Chinese Natural History drawings said to be a perfect blend between the needs of the naturalist for accuracy and details and the inspiration of the artist.

(John Reeves (1774–1856) was employed from 1812 to 1831 as Inspector of Taxes at the East India Company's factory in Canton.)

This book retailed at a price of £150.

Changes in 1974–5 – Trying to Hold the Field

In the year of 1974, Mr Colin Stockwell (formerly sales executive) was appointed sales manager and the company bought another press.

Mr Lawrence Cullimore was asked to see the Consul litho press and to advise on its suitability for rotary collotype. As his comments were favourable, steps were taken to accommodate this 60″ x 40″ press and to adjust it for our requirements.

One half of the press room was required for this large machine, entailing the dismantling of a row of three presses. It was then manpowered into the mill by removing the left hand front window and the brick work below it. The press was positioned the length of the room and was totally enclosed, working as a separate unit for humidity control.

The window and brickwork were replaced as soon as possible.

We were printing a number of colour jobs but although of great prestige value, the high standard of work for facsimile reproduction made for a low profit margin.

The sheets of coins also lost ground. Here we were challenged by screenless litho. This was a cheaper method than collotype but of lesser quality – some customers being more motivated by cost than perfection.

We Print Artificial Eyes for the National Health Service

An unusual job which suited collotype admirably was the printing of artificial eyes. This work was carried out on order from the NHS in Norwich and supplied via their Blackpool department.

The many variations open to collotype as well as the lack of 'grain' made the process most acceptable for the making and matching of artificial eyes for human patients.

There were fourteen basic eye patterns and five basic eye sizes from 10.75mm to 11.75mm in 0.25mm increments. We printed them in blue-grey, grey, hazel and brown.

1977 Brings Redundancies

The workforce were informed more redundancies would have to be made. Although not entirely a shock, none of us really wanted to leave. Some had been with the company all their working lives.

We were offered early retirement with a pension, or a lump sum with a reduced pension.

Frank Wathen – An Able Printer with a Flair for Engineering

At this time of redundancies Mr Frank Wathen, who had joined the company in 1924, also finished. Unfortunately he was taken ill shortly afterwards and died.

He had worked in the letterpress department until the 1939 war, when he was directed to Parnells, Yate on essential war work. On his return he worked in the same department for a few years.

He had helped Mr Harry Russell get our first gravure press printing when it was initially set up in the green shed. Later, some of the small staff running it were moved to the empty Brooke Bond factory at Charfield. After a few successful years there, he returned to Wotton when the Brookeside factory was completed in 1959. Although of a quiet disposition, he was a very popular person in both factories, always willing to help in times of difficulties. For many years he rode the same BSA motorcycle to work.

Frank's father, William Wathen, owned a tin smith's shop opposite the Bear Street Garage, where many household products and items for the various local mills were made. William Wathen had learnt his trade at Plomers at the bottom of Long Street (a large kettle hangs from the wall, evidence of the trade once carried out there).

More Moves and Management Changes – Brookeside

Once again the finishing department was moved – this time it was to the green shed. The space vacated in Trident by this move was taken over by Brookeside as a storage department. Unlike collotype, they used large quantities of reeled paper.

In 1978 Mr Philip Brooke and Mr Cyril Wellings were appointed joint managing directors of Brookeside.

Our Final Colour Work

The same year saw a very nice job printed called *Views of Richmond Etchings and Engravings* for Bamber Gascoigne.

Also being printed were a number of sheets of black and white postcards. These were reproduced from old photos collected from museums and libraries. These proved a very popular line.

The last major job printed at Britannia Mill in 1980 was for the Post Office. These were various addresses to cover the many areas of an envelope and were printed in 500 editions to check the high speed franking machines being produced for the Post Office sorting departments.

Over the last years of collotype at Wotton, we had the privilege of printing for Robert van Nice of Dunbarton Oakes, USA.

The printing consisted of many of the original drawings to complete a huge book (37" x 34") of the St Sophia Mosque in Istanbul. The company was eventually chosen because of the accuracy in achieving the fine line drawing needed.

Closure of the Cotswold Collotype Co. Ltd.

The closure of the Cotswold Collotype Company occurred on 7 November 1980. The total numbers being employed at this time were down to fourteen. It was a very sad day for many of us who had enjoyed working for the company for so many years and had felt part of it. We had all tried throughout to use our best skills, ideas and ingenuity to build it up, enlarge its scope of work and even in its latter days had fought hard to keep it from closure.

Also, about that time, it was with great regret that we learned of the death of Mr John Brooke, one-time chairman of all companies in the Group. He had paid several visits to our company and had worked for Brooke Bond in various capacities all his life. On the occasion of the company's Jubilee he had presented Mr Frank Wathen with his gold watch for long service.

In Limbo – The Hopes of a Rescuer

There now ensued a period of waiting and wondering who would buy the collotype business. One thing was certain, it would no longer operate from Britannia Mill. The building was due for demolition owing to structural defects.

Several people were interested in the collotype process and they were expected to retain the remaining staff. Eventually, the choice was narrowed down, and a Mr Royston Capel finally bought the business and he met all the staff at the Swan Hotel, Wotton.

The business would have to trade under a different name. Three of the old flatbed presses were taken to Spring Mill, Avening Road, Nailsworth along with the Consul Albert press to operate under a new name.

From Wotton-Under-Edge to Nailsworth – Cotswold Fine Arts

Work started on 27 May 1981 at Nailsworth under the name Cotswold Fine Arts. Its first job was to complete a book called *Spanish Coins and Medals* that had been abandoned at Wotton.

The interior of the factory was custom built to accommodate the collotype process and had a humidity controlled printing room.

A new 24″ x 24″ Japanese darkroom camera was installed, along with automatic negative developing units.

Mr Philip Brooke supervised the running of the business at Nailsworth for a short while until his retirement.

Printing Ends

Printing advertised as collotype ended in March 1986. Finally trading finished early in 1987. September of that year saw the whole of the equipment put up for sale, the presses going for scrap.

During my working life at least half a dozen collotype firms closed. Although a beautiful process, it was expensive to produce.

The staff had now dwindled to three – Harold Maunders, Victor Jellings and a young lady in the office.

Although the collotype process is finished in this country, it is good to know the work produced can be found all over the world, and in many museums and universities in this country.

Even the humble postcard, the bread and butter of the company, is eagerly sought after, many now valued in pounds.

I was asked by Sandoe, Luce & Panes to help catalogue the camera equipment and lenses, some of which had been in use by

Friths at Charfield and which I had used while with the company. I bought the Kodak Precision Enlarger for my own use.

Some collotype is believed to be used in Vienna and certainly in America.

In 1988, Britannia Mill, home of the Cotswold Collotype from 1912 until 1980, was demolished.

Like many others, I spent the whole of my working life of forty-eight years with the company. Since retiring, and having time to reflect, I have a feeling of great satisfaction of being well treated and having worked among pleasant workmates.

We printed a variety of interesting work, plenty of which is about today throughout the world.

Although collotype is finished in this country, we have the satisfaction of lasting the longest.

Out of collotype sprang the Berkshire Gravure Company which is doing very well.

A collotype man, Mr Harry Russell, son of one of the original directors, with ready help from the Berkshire Printing Company, was largely responsible for starting the gravure process at Wotton, as previously mentioned.

The real spirit of the Cotswold Collotype died at the closure at Wotton in 1980. Although collotype was carried on for a short while at Nailsworth, the spirit developed by the directors and staff at Britannia Mill was never rekindled.

In hindsight, apart from the loss of jobs, it would have been better if the business had finished altogether at Wotton, making a much happier ending.

Appendices

1. Here is a list of the companies and organisations that used collotype for postcard illustrations:

Friths
Kimble
Judges
Lofthouse Crosbie
Tilley
Coates
Dennis Moss
Wm. Ritchie
Skilton
Kimlock
Burrows
Natural History Museum, London
Millar & Lang

Valentines
Butler
Harvey Barton
Thridgould
Catling
Strange
Pearson
Shoesmith & Etheridge
The Grange Publishing Co.
Maysons
Ashmolean Museum, Oxford
Raphael Tuck

These are the major companies that had postcards reproduced. The list does not include a few museums and the many private shops and individuals who had a minimum number of views and quantities printed (possibly as low as 250 copies as an edition).

2. When collo colours were first introduced:-

September 1950
November 1950
September 1953
October 1954

1st Valentines sheet
1st Millar & Lang sheet
1st Frith sheet
Mention of 1st double varnished PC sheet

3. Publishing companies and societies using collotype

Chatto & Windus
Faber & Faber

Cambridge University Press
J.W. Arrowsmiths

HMSO
Macmillan
Buchanan
Hogarth Press
N Kaye Ltd. (book illust.)
Murray
Methuen
Routledge
Cassells & Co.
Lund Humphries
Adlards
British Museum
Westerham Press
Batsford
Hart Davies
Jarrold
Rubens
Spinks (coins)
A.H. Baldwins (coins)
E.S.G. Robinson
Piercey & Biggs
Crown Agents
R.A.G. Carson
R. & R. Clark
Berkshire Publishing Co.
Wilson Peck (coins)
Catling
Bloesch
Manchester University Press
Numismatic Chronicles
New Zealand Government
Malacological Society
University of Glasgow
Commonwealth of Australia
Geological Society of London
Royal Society of Victoria, Australia
University of Melbourne
Lord Nuffield Press
The Clarenden Press (coins)

Glendinning & Co.
Carey & Claridge Ltd.
The Shenval Press
Liverpool Letterpress
Robert Stockwell Ltd.
Christie, Manson & Woods
The Folio Society
Pitman Press
Country Life Ltd.
The Ryerson Press, Toronto
The Gregg Press
Charles Skilton
The Athlone Press
Dobson Books Ltd.
Hutchinsons Pub. Ltd.
T. Gerrard & Co.
Hazell, Watson & Viney
Ashmolean Museum
Geological Society
Penrose Annual
The Corsetry Journal
Palaeontographical Society
Cousland (coins)
Edinburgh Bibliographical
   Society
Gold Coast Geological Society
Hebrew University
Royal Society, Edinburgh
Aberdeen University Press
Eugrammia Press
Academic Press
Northumberland Press
McLaren
Constable & Co.
Leicester University
Alec Tiranti Ltd
Nattali & Maurice
Artistic Publications
Holland Press

Coats Ltd.
Palaeontological Society
Phaidon Press
Dunbarton Oaks
Prints International
The Bodley Head
A. & C. Black
Yorkshire Geological Society

Martin Orskey
Gregg Press
Ottawa
Hamlyn Group
MEXE
Osprey
Blackwell
Oxford University Press

4. Staff employed: 1910–20s

Mr F. R. Jeater	director
Mr C. R. Bagwell	director
Mr H. J. Russell	director
Mr C. Russell	collotype printer
Mr F. Russell	collotype printer
Mr C. Beale	collotype printer
Mr A. Philpott	
Mr J. Roach	
Miss Harding	
Miss Hollister (Mrs. E. Smith)	
Miss H. Gibbard	
Mr J. Goscombe	collotype apprentice
Mr H. Russell Jnr.	collotype apprentice
Miss E. Gibbard	

5. Staff employed: 1930–31

Directors:
Mr C. R. Bagwell
Mr F. E. Frith

Mr F. R. Jeater
Mr H. J. Russell

Mr G. Underhill	platemaker
Miss M. Carter	negative retoucher
Mr H. Miller	print retoucher
Miss M. Malone	finisher
Miss B. Wyatt	Bromide cards
Miss E. Dolman	finisher

Miss V. Reynolds	Bromide cards
Miss H. Gibbard	finisher
Mr W. White	guillotine operator
Mr E. Hurlock	packer
Mrs. E. Warmington	finisher
Mr H. Russell Jnr.	printer
Mr C. Russell	printer
Mr F. Russell	printer
Mr C. Beale	printer
Miss E. Cornock	press feeder
Miss D. Russell	press feeder
Miss P. Wyatt	press feeder
Miss E. Sharpe	press feeder
Miss A. Savage	general duties
Mr F. Wathen	letterpress printer
Mr S. Davis	letterpress printer
Mr K. Goulding	apprentice printer
Mr A. Lusty	Bromide printer
Mrs. E. Smith	Bromide printer
Mr J. Goscombe	printer
Miss E. Gibbard	finisher
Mr D. Emes	negative retoucher
Miss E. Carter	press feeder
Miss M. Butler	press feeder

6. Staff employed: early 1950s

Mr J. Goscombe	printer
Mr B. Fryer	letterpress department
Mr G. Underhill	platemaker
Mr S. Cole	printer
Mr F. Russell	printer
Miss D. Dye	press feeder
Mr F. Wathen	L/P printer
Miss B. Bailey	finisher
Mr W. White	guillotine operator
Miss J. Martin	press feeder
Miss P. Wyatt	I/C finishing
Miss M. Yates	colourist

Mr J. Mabon	packer
Miss N. Hurcombe	colourist
Mr R. Woodward	printer
Miss E. Mundy	finisher
Mr W. Durn	office staff
Miss J. Barton	colourist
Mr S. Davis	L/P printer
Miss A. Martin	
Mr D. Emes	camera operator
Miss S. Lampitt	
Mr A. Pitcher	office staff
Miss M. Gale	colourist
Mr R. Hardy	artists department
Miss H. Robinson	colourist
Mr L. Smith	printer
Miss A. Barton	colourist
Mr E. Peglar	guillotine operator
Miss H. Mabon	press feeder
Mr F. Smart	platemaking
Mr J. Frith	artists department
Mr L. Nicholls	printer
Mr H. Maunders	camera operator
Mr R. Dancox	artists department
Mr V. Jellings	artists department
Mr A. Moreman	letterpress department
Mr R. Brain	printer
Mr J. Price	printer
Mr C. Russell	printer
Mr D. Hopkins	platemaking
Mr C. Beale	printer

7. Staff employed including Brookeside: 1950

Mr F. E. Frith JP	Miss J. Hurcombe	Miss V. Walker
Mr H. Russell JP	Mr F. Russell	Miss J. Stevens
Mr P. Brooke	Mr W. Durn	Mr F. Smart
Mr J. Goscombe	Miss P. Wyatt	Mr L. Cullimore
Mr W. White	Mr H. Maunders	Miss S. Birt
Miss J. Glenny	Miss E. Mundy	Mr D. Merrett

Mr J. Jeffrey
Miss P. Smith
Mr G. Smith
Miss C. Timbrell
Mr R. Woodward
Miss E. Eacott
Mr J. Mabon
Miss L. Cross
Mr G. Underhill
Mr C. Beale
Miss H. Mabon
Mr M. Crew
Miss P. Sharpe
Mr R. Hewish
Miss R. Evans
Mr G. Bleaken
Miss P. Fry
Mr R. Brain
Miss J. Cullimore
Mr M. Hughes
Miss M. Wilkins
Miss O. Mabon

Mr E. Peglar
Miss W. Hayward
Mr B. Fryer
Miss L. Pearce
Mr D. Emes
Miss M. Clarke
Mr A. Moreman
Miss J. Dix
Mr R. Hardy
Miss R. Diment
Mr J. Portlock
Mr M. Cole
Mr H. Hurcombe
Mr B. Candy
Miss C. Evans
Mr J. Price
Miss A. Shellard
Mr S. Cole
Miss A. Martin
Mr J. Mabbett
Miss S. Robson
Mr P. Neale

Miss H. Butcher
Mr R. Alway
Miss J. Warrell
Mr C. Foxwell
Miss M. Birt
Mr E. Goodfield
Miss J. Beale
Mr V. Jellings
Miss J. Morgan
Mr B. Lawrence
Miss J. Stevens
Mr F. Wathen
Mr L. Smith Snr.
Mr P. Barton
Mr M. Davis
Mr L. Smith Jnr.
Mr C. Russell
Mr L. Nicholls
Miss R. Chappell
Mr R. Dancox
Mr S. Davis

8. Staff employed at the closure of the company: August 1980

Mrs J. Luker
Miss P. Lottinga
Mr H. Maunders
Mr R. Hardy
Mr D. Hopkins
Mr T. Luker
Mr V. Jellings

Mrs J. Sims
Miss J. Pearce
Mrs J. Young
Mr L. Smith
Mr B. Candy
Mr N. Todd
Mr D. Taylor

9. Cotswold Publishing Co. Ltd. 1907–08 trading accounts.

For Year ending June 30ᵗʰ 1908.

1908 June 30	Stock on Hand :—				
	Paper, Cardboard, Cards & Madeup				
	Goods	239.14.5			
	Films & Plates	29.3.10			
	Chemicals, Colouring & Printing Ink	34.5.11		303 4 2	
	Material used :—				
	Paper, Cardboard, Cards & Madeup				
	Goods	455.16.0			
	Films & Plates	55.1.10			
	Chemicals, Colouring & Printing Ink	63.7.8			
	Photographs	3.4.6		557 10 —	
				860 14 2	
	Sales	1911.17.4			
	less :— Returns & Trade discounts	179.12.1		1732 5 3	
	Discounts Received			14 8 2	
	Commission on collection of Frith's				
	Book Debts			9 5 6	
			Forward.	1755 18 11	

Trading & Profit & Loss Accounts

Forward		1594	10 3
Postages & Telegrams		12	16 7
Repairs & Renewals		34	1 6
Audit fees & Preparation of accounts		9	9 .
Bank Interest & Charges		13	5 11
Bad Debts		30	1 7
Discounts allowed	11.10.1		
do reserved	8. 5.11	19	16 .
Interest on Loans		4	6 6
Interest on Partners Capital		24	17 7
Removal Expenses – Proportion written off (on basis of 5 years)		16	9 6
Expenditure on Lease & Buildings – Proportion written off (on basis of 14 years from Sept 1902)		6	3 11
Depreciation of Machinery, Fittings & Fixtures 7½% on £400	30.0.0		
15% on £105	15.15.0	45	15 .
505			
		1871	13 4

for Year ending June 30ᵗʰ 1908.

Forward			1755 18 11
Rent of Premises sublet:-			
Sharpfield	2·10·0		
Warman	1·10·0		
Greenwood	2·5·0		
Brown	18 3	6 16 3	
Balance being Nett Loss on Trading			
divisible as under:-			
J. R. Bagwell	16·6·1		
H. J. Russell	16·6·1		
F. Slater	16·6·0	48 18 2	
			1811 13 4

Balance Sheet   as   at

— Liabilities —

Creditors :-

On open accounts	451.19.0	
Bills payable	37.18.0	
Accrued Charges etc	37.9.7	527 6 7

Loan Creditors :-

Firth & Co Ltd	189.12.9	
J. Lucas loan & interest	102.13.2	
D. Parker diffo	101.13.4	393 19 3

Capital accounts :-

C. R. Bagwell Capital introduced	218.7.5		
Interest	9.3.2		
	227.10.7		
less : drawings	4.10.0		
share of loss	16.6.1	20.16.1	206 14 6

H. J. Russell . Capital introduced	200.0.0		
Interest	8.10.10		
	208.10.10		
less : share of loss	16.6.1		192 4 9

F. Seater . Capital introduced	150.0.0		
Interest	7.3.7		
	157.3.7		
less : drawings	13.0.9		
share of loss	16.6.0	29.6.9	127 16 10

Forward	1448 1 11

30ᵗʰ June. 1908

— Assets —

Stock on Hand :- Goods & Material	275.13.4			
Coke	6.1			
Films	27.10.10		303	10 8
Machinery Fittings, Fixtures &				
Utensils Taken over from Firth & Co Ld	575.0.0			
less :- depreciation	45.15.0			
Sales of Machinery	96.16.3	142.11.3		
		362.8.9		
Additions during Year	111.14.6		474	3 3
Book Debts :-				
Ordinary	323.7.6			
less 2½ % reserve	8.5.11			
		315.1.7		
Firth & Co Ld Debt	132.10.8			
Outstanding acct &				
payments in advance	14.5.3		461	17 6
Cash at Bank	32.7.4			
do in Hand	17.3		33	4 7
Lease & Buildings Account :-				
Expenditure as per schedule	115.11.10			
less :- written off against				
Trading Account	6.3.11			
			109	7 11
Forward			1382	3 11

Balance Sheet as at

Statistics

Forward · 14481 · 11

14481 · 11

I have prepared the above Accounts and
and certify the same to be correct. I have
on hand my £ 303.10.8

J.G. Taylor

Chartered Accountant
Bristol

July 13ᵗʰ 1908

30th June 1908

— Assets —

Forward			1382 3 11
Removal Expenses - as per schedule	82.7.6		
Less - written off against Trading a/c	16.9.6	65 18	
			1448 1 11

Balance Sheet from the books of the Company
accepted your figures for the value of the Stock

Signatures of
Partners

CRBagwell
A. Russell
Fredk. Jeaffer

17 July 1908

10. Building Plans

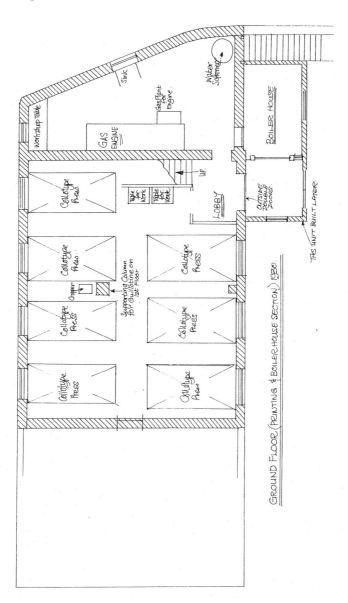

GROUND FLOOR (PRINTING & BOILER HOUSE SECTION) 1930

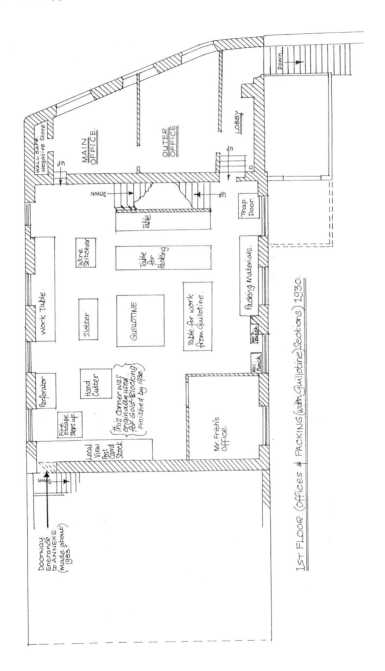

1ST FLOOR (Offices & Packing (with Guillotine) Sections) 1930.

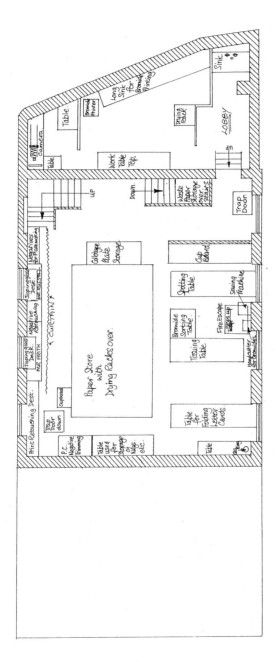

2ND FLOOR (Camera, Retouching & Finishing Sections.) 1930.

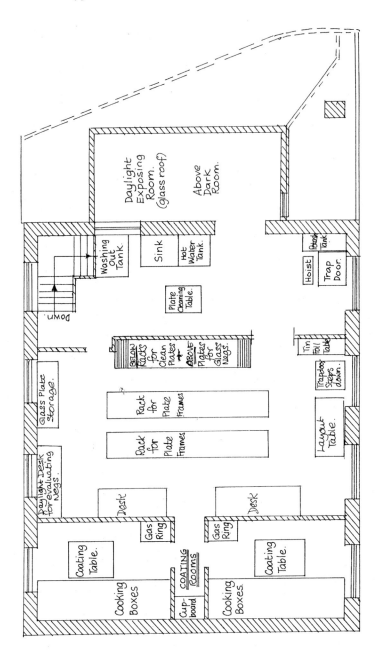

3RD FLOOR (Platemaking Section) 1930.

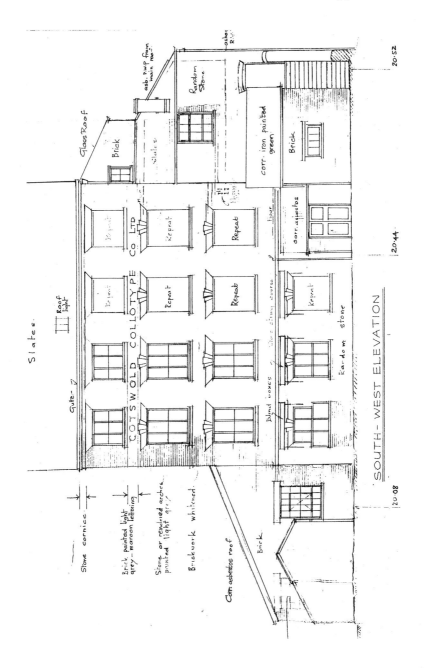

SOUTH-WEST ELEVATION

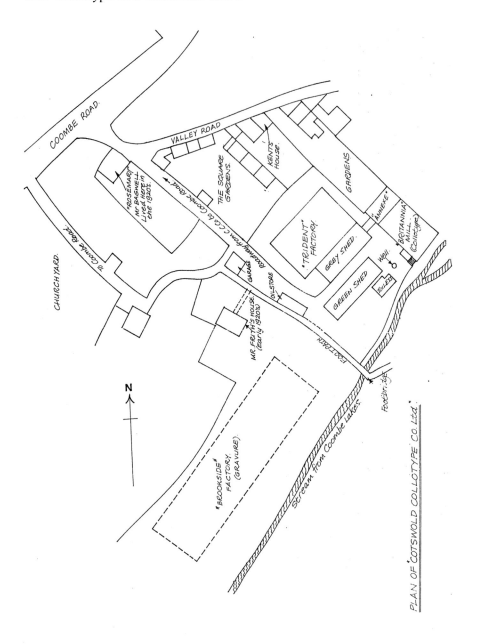

PLAN OF "COTSWOLD COLLOTYPE CO. Ltd."